Presence

What if Jesus Were Really Here?

R. Thomas Ashbrook

Library of Congress Cataloguing-in-Publication Data
Ashbrook, R. Thomas
Presence: What if Jesus Were Really Here? / R. Thomas Ashbrook
Library of Congress Control Number: 2014922420

ISBN 978-0-9916368-1-5
1.   Spiritual Formation. 2. Christian Fiction. 3. Inspiration

Printed in the United States of America
First Edition

Acknowledgements

Then He said to me, "Son of man, eat what you find; eat this scroll, and go, speak to the house of Israel." So I opened my mouth, and He fed me this scroll. He said to me, "Son of man, feed your stomach and fill your body with this scroll which I am giving you." Then I ate it, and it was sweet as honey in my mouth. Ezek 3:1-3

Some authors write because they love artistry with their native language. Others desire to communicate the inspiration of their thinking and to convince others to think similarly. For me, writing feels more like the gestation and delivery of some aspect of the heart of God, commanded within me with the compulsion to endure what feels like labor pains to give it birth. As with any birth, this work emerged floundering to find its own voice, in hope of accomplishing the purpose for which its Creator intended it. In my delivery of this sweet scroll, the Lord brought others who also listened to the heart of God and helped the message mature and develop.

I must first acknowledge my great gratitude for the One who filled my mouth and inner being with His Presence and with this story. My deep appreciation goes out to the *Imago Christi* Community for their partnership and support in helping me read the scroll, discerning the Lord's intent. As *Presence* began to take shape, the Lord brought many people able to edit and fashion the English language. For the first draft, a whole host of family and friends gave feedback and suggestions. Then for the second, Jeff Sweeney, Arlene Kampe, Anita Shehi, and Pat LaPlante spent many hours editing. A special thanks to Pastor David Dillon for his masterful cover design. David's artistic abilities span many forms, but always reflect the creativity of his Master. I also want to thank Roy Graham, a member of the Order of Imago Christi, for his help with content formatting and design and Carter Zimmerman for his marketing expertise in helping to make this work known and available. Finally, my deep gratitude to my wife, Charlotte, for her loving encouragement, support, patience, and sacrifice through the five year gestation and birth process of *Presence*.

Table of Contents

Preface

People of all religions and non-religions yearn, even if secretly, for a real God, a personal God they can relate to. Instead of religion, we want an actual relationship with a personal God who we find somehow, knowable, experienceable, and most of all, present and involved. We Christians insist that such a relationship is possible with God, the creator of the universe, through His Son, Jesus, and the Holy Spirit given to enable us to believe. Yet I propose that few actually find such a relationship real.

In recent decades, Christians have fled churches in droves, leaving beautiful stained glass cathedrals in the hands of realtors who sell them for tourist attractions or museums. While once the fear of hell and the promise of "heaven-when-we-die" sufficed to keep people going to church, now for many, the endless stream of words about a God we never experience leaves us dry, discouraged, and disillusioned. Religion, even the Christian religion, seems irrelevant and empty to many.

In these same decades, however, people travel thousands of miles just to stand in the spot where Jesus walked or to see the places where a miracle happened. Jerusalem, the Sea of Galilee, Patmos, Rome, Iona, Assisi, and countless shrines attract thousands of visitors every year. Why do people go there? This pilgrimage phenomena involves more than Christians. I believe that people of every religion, even atheists, want something more out of life than what appears to be their typical lifecycle; they're looking, instinctively, for something or someone that transcends it, which gives their span of years meaning and purpose.

Ultimately, we long to somehow mingle our physical here-and-now existence with the mystical reality of the One who created our universe, the One who can provide some sort of order out of the chaos that appears to be our lot. We want to do more than believe in a God; we want to experience Him. Interestingly, the God of Abraham, Isaac and Jacob, the God of the Bible turns out to be the only "God" who offers to let us know Him—in Jesus. While some may feel "safe" with a God "up there" or "out there," I think that most of us, even secretly, want more. We want the world we live in and the world that Jesus lives in to intersect, merge to the point where we feel a touching, a knowing, and a life-changing Love. We wonder what it would be like to experience His touch, hear the sound of His voice, become captured by His gaze, and to be held in His embrace. It's the kind of relationship with God that we're created for; it's why the Word of God became flesh and blood. Know it or not, we long for Jesus; we yearn to experience His wonder and grandeur, the love and power of His Presence— Emmanuel—God with us. Is such a desire wishful thinking, reality avoidance, or bad theology? I don't think so. After all, it's what we teach. So, whatever happened to a personal relationship with Jesus?

The birth, life, death, and resurrection of Jesus of Nazareth clearly represent the most life and culture-changing event in human history. God came to us as a human being who spoke to us directly, showing us the love and power of God and offering us a new relationship of knowing Him. We call it the incarnation. For those who come to know Jesus personally, God gives His Holy Spirit so that the same communion between Jesus and the Father can become ours as well. In relationship with Jesus, the "Son of Man," we can actually experience God.

No longer do we have to try to understand God only as the eternal and transcendent Creator, the One who fills all time and space. We can now relate to this eternal spiritual God in a way similar to the way we relate to another human person. This "Son of Man" feels joy and pain like we do, was tempted in every way that we are tempted. He died on the cross for the forgiveness of our sins. Jesus invites us to become daughters and sons of the most High God. He offers Himself as our Shepherd, promising never to leave us or forsake us. Jesus remained a human being even after His resurrection and ascension so that we could continue to relate to God in ways we mere humans can understand. The apostle John put it this way:

> What was from the beginning, what we have heard, what we have seen with our eyes, what we beheld and our hands handled, concerning the Word of Life—and the life was manifested, and we have seen and bear witness and proclaim to you the eternal life, which was with the Father and was manifested to us—what we have seen and heard we proclaim to you also, that you also may have fellowship with us; and indeed our fellowship is with the Father, and with His Son Jesus Christ. And these things we write, so that our joy may be made complete. (1 John 1:1-4)

John goes on to invite us into the same relationship and experience of God in Jesus.

Whatever happened to Jesus, the man? To be sure, our relationship with Jesus changed after His resurrection. Yet His followers encountered him on the road to Emmaus, in a locked room, and on many other occasions. After His ascension followers such as Paul reported meeting Him and being taught by Him. John the apostle encountered Jesus on the island of Patmos. But we have to honestly ask ourselves if we still experience Him as alive and with us in the same way that people in the Book of Acts described or the writings of the apostles revealed Him? Has He been locked between the leather covers of the Bible, permitted to speak only through its printed words? Has Jesus been somehow encased in statues and paintings that represent our imaginings of His likeness? Did Jesus' throne, at the right hand of God, get moved? Is the Kingdom of God no longer in our midst, but lodged in some far galaxy light years away or in some other dimension?

If Jesus dwells present with us, if the Kingdom of God is here, then why do our church services so often feel more like a memorial service to a historical figure who lived so long ago rather than a celebration with our Lord who's actually in the room? Have we forgotten that Jesus still resides with us? Maybe His words, "… and I will be with you, even to the end of the age," no longer ring in our ears. Could it be that we learned to relate to a Book rather than to the Son of God. Has our "faith" become focused on a history, a doctrine, a ritual, and an eternal promise rather than upon the person of Jesus, in whom the fullness of God dwells, who resides present with us— Emmanuel?

"Yes, yes," some may say, "I believe that Jesus is here, at least a 'here' that's mainly up there somewhere." (The Scriptures were written in a culture that pictured the world as flat, with God living in a heaven above. Our understanding of the earth and the universe has changed, but even then Jesus taught that "the Kingdom of God has come near us" and the apostle Paul told the Athenians that "in Him we live and move and have our being." Therefore we need to understand the "ups and downs" in Scripture in their cultural context.) Of course God is "up there" and "down here." God fills all time and space—transcendent, omnipresent. But He is also immanent—Present. "All time and space" is not just out there—the Kingdom of God has come to us and still remains. But I wonder if we know that truth merely as doctrine rather than experience. I wonder if we've confused a relationship with the Bible or the church with a relationship with the person of Jesus.

There remains a further problem. If we really do believe that Jesus is "here," do we have any idea how to recognize His presence, to communicate with Him, to enter into a personal relationship of love with Him? If not, we make His presence all but irrelevant. He may be trying to shepherd and lead us, but is it possible that we're too spiritually blind and deaf to see or hear Him?

Recent history has been filled with new attempts to regain this personal relationship with Jesus. The Holy Spirit has been trying to scrape away the religious scales from our eyes so that we might actually see and experience God—with us. The Reformation helped us begin to get our theology back on course and more recently the Jesus movement, the Small Group movement, the Charismatic movement, and now the Spiritual Formation movement have brought new life and hope for many. Each of these movements of God has helped us get a better glimpse of what we long for. The Jesus movement challenged us to refocus on the person of Jesus and relationship with God in Him. The Small Group movement invited us to relate together with the person of Jesus, to experience Him in community. The Charismatic movement called us to follow God in the power of Jesus through the Holy Spirit. Experiences of healing, prophecy, and the other spiritual gifts demonstrated the presence of God with us, countering many people's view of Him as a distant deity who looks down from afar.

In the Spiritual Formation movement God challenges us to recall the ancient Christian experiences of passionate love for Jesus and the spiritual practices that help us attend to His presence with us. Its emphasis on spiritual growth invites us closer to a real relationship with Jesus and describes the transformation that can happen within us through the work of the Holy Spirit. However, many of us get lost in the mystical language and metaphors that still make us feel that God resides up there or out there someplace, visiting us only under

5

controlled circumstances. While the Spiritual Formation movement encourages us to become more Christ-like through spiritual practices, we often get focused on ourselves and what we do, rather than God. Even though our motivations may be right, I wonder if most of us don't really know what to expect of Jesus <u>in the midst</u> of these spiritual disciplines.

I suggest, however, that our quest for a real and personal God should begin where God began in reclaiming us from our fall into sin and death. God loved us so much that He sent His Son, Jesus, as a human being, a man. Maybe we should return there, relating to Emmanuel as a man, this Man who embodies the fullness of God, who resides with us—Present. Jesus told us that we experience the Father when we experience Jesus. The Apostle John saw the resurrected Jesus as a man, glorious and magnificent, but still a man. The writer of Hebrews declared, in the thirteenth chapter, verse 8, that "Jesus is the same yesterday and today and forever."

If He is in fact present with us, shouldn't we be able to relate to Him in a way similar to his first His disciples? Shouldn't we be able to listen to Him, talk to Him, and interact with Him in practical ways? Isn't that the kind of communication that Jesus intended when He said that His sheep hear His voice and follow Him? "But how can we do that?" you may be asking. "His disciples could actually see and hear Him. They could touch Him and feel His presence. We don't know how to see, hear, or touch spiritually. We just can't expect a Jesus <u>that</u> real."

While I understand those objections and struggle with them myself, I wonder if God would promise something that can't really happen, something He is not willing to deliver. No, I suppose not. But where would we start? How can we learn to experience Jesus as present?

Let's start with the Scriptures. Let's observe how Jesus taught people to experience more of Him than they could see and touch. In the Gospels, we read that Jesus used parables or stories. He invited his hearers to imagine a familiar scene and to see a truth in it, one deeper than they could have previously known without His help. He used stories about shepherds, farmers, merchants, clergymen, fishermen, women and children in real and familiar situations to demonstrate some aspect of our relationship with Him.

Maybe it would be helpful, with the guidance of the Holy Spirit, to use our own imaginations. If we stop to think about it, we realize that our imaginations have, in fact, helped us come to know more about Jesus in the past. As we have read about Jesus in the Gospels, we imagined the scene as it was described; we heard Jesus speaking and imaginatively let Him speak to us. We watched His behavior and noticed how we responded. We sensed that He was talking directly to us, took His words literally, and then discovered that they were true in us as well as in the original hearers. While that kind of imagination can be a good start, it can still leave Jesus in the past, with us far away in the present. So, we might try going further in our imaginative endeavor.

What if we used our imaginations to interact with that same Jesus, the one we've come to know in Scripture, in the present? Maybe an imaginative story about Jesus relating to everyday people in our time could give us a feel for what it might be like for us to experience Jesus as present in our own lives, day-to-day. With that taste for Jesus as present, it might become easier to open ourselves to Him in the here and now, in practical ways. With such an imaginary story as a common experience, we could then reflect on what we've discovered and learned from Him together. Let's give it a try. Let me tell you a story.

"Once upon a time…"

Chapter1: Encounters

At exactly 3:47A.M, James Cline, pastor of Emmaus Community Church, gasped and sat straight up in bed, shaking. It startled Kate who sleepily leaned over and said, "What's wrong Jim? Are you alright?"

"Nothing, honey; go back to sleep." She turned over and slowly reengaged her dream. But there was no sleep left in Jim. "Was that a dream?" he asked himself. "Never had a dream like that before. Couldn't be a dream—too real. Impossible. Maybe I'm still dreaming." He pinched his arm till it hurt. "I'm awake," he grimaced. He just sat and stared at the corner of the softly moonlight filled room wondering if it, whatever it was, would happen again. Then he lay down and tried to go back to sleep, but to no avail. He felt totally awake, maybe more awake than he had ever been in his whole life. "Jesus is this real?" he prayed. No answer; just the silence of the bedroom, the white moonlight, and a thousand questions.

Jim began to recall the "dream" or whatever it was. He had been sleeping; he knew that much. He seldom slept well, often tossing and turning. But this night he recalled being awakened from a sound sleep by a voice calling his name.

"Jim, I'd like to talk to you. Wake up, please."

He dimly remembered rubbing the sleep from his eyes, throwing his feet over the side of the bed, and standing up. He saw the hazy form of a man standing in the corner of the room. Jim couldn't see his face because of the light flooding the room from behind him. Staring and squinting to get a better look, he could barely make out a simple gold crown on the man's head. Surprisingly, Jim didn't feel frightened. The visitor's demeanor radiated warmth, safety, and even friendship. As Jim squinted into the fog, trying to see a bit more clearly, he heard a firm masculine voice.

"I'm aware of your frustrations, Jim, and I want to help. I'd like us to sit down and talk, just the two of us. Here is my proposition: I'll meet with you physically—face to face, today at 3:45pm in your office. You cannot tell anyone, not even Kate, about this experience now, or about our meetings later. In fact, you can never ever tell anyone. If you even start to tell, I'll erase your memory of our encounters, and you'll never even recall that this happened. If you're up to the "face to face," under these conditions, be in your office with the door closed. You might even give your secretary the afternoon off." Then the figure smiled and simply blinked away.

Jim laid back down and started to return to sleep. Then suddenly he sat up in bed again. Not sure whether he'd dreamed the event or saw the vision while awake, he stared at the corner of the bedroom. He could still hear the voice in his head, the words seeming to have imprinted themselves on his mind. "Frustrations? Want to help? Face to face? Why? Was it Jesus or an angel… or maybe even the devil? No. If it, or He, was real, then He was surely Jesus. Whoever stood in the corner of the bedroom knew me through and through, and loved me; I could feel it. It wasn't the devil, that's for sure."

Jim pulled on his robe and grabbed for his journal to write it all down and then caught himself, "No, what if someone reads it?" He stopped and grimaced at himself, "This is crazy; Jesus doesn't wake people up in the middle of the night and invite them to a meeting."

Jim's earlier than usual shower, shave, and dressing swirled with confusion, thought, laughter, mumbling to himself, and dumbfounded silence. He almost shaved twice. While never before giving two thoughts about what he wore to work, now he couldn't decide whether to wear a suit (which he never wore to the office) or slacks and a sport shirt or.... "This is stupid! I have a silly dream and now I'm trying to decide what to wear for a meeting with the Savior of the World." He kissed Kate good-by, trying not to exchange too direct a look, and took off early for church.

ဆဆ ‌ေ‌ေ

Lillian Frank had just turned the corner from Broadway onto Second. In a hurry and late for almost everything that day, she'd managed to collect the kids from Emmaus Consolidated School just in time to avoid making the teacher stay late to watch them. She grabbed a few groceries, picked up the dry cleaning, and now headed like a drag racer to soccer practice. In the back seat, Evan poked Beth who produced a shrill vibrato that could have cracked the windshield, "Don't touch me!"

"Quiet!' Lillian yelled, turning her head. As she glanced forward again, she spotted a figure walking from between two parked cars and stepping right in front of her car. Tires screeched, groceries and dry cleaning flew, and a loud thud told Lillian that something terrible had happened. "Be quiet and stay in the car!" Lillian jumped out terrified to discover what or who must be lying on the pavement, probably in a pool of blood. The discovery would change her life, forever.

"Oh my God, are you all right?" Lillian yelled as she helped the young man, no blood to be seen, to his feet.

"Oh, I'm fine. Been through a lot worse than this. Sorry to give you such a start, but it was the only way I could get you to stop long enough to talk to me."

Lillian stared in disbelief as the young man brushed the dust from his jeans and straightened his hair. "Shall I call 911," Lillian asked, reaching for her cell phone?

"Heavens no. I'm not hurt at all. But that dent in the hood of your car will have to be fixed."

11

Lillian stuttered, "I'm so sorry; I looked away at the kids for a split second."

He smiled back, "Yeah, you came a little closer to these cars than I expected. I really just meant to flag you down and hand you this message," stuffing an envelope into her hand.

Lillian now faced the stranger, her eyes locked on his. "You nearly got yourself killed to hand me a message? That's ridiculous!"

"Oh, I've already gotten myself killed for you, Lillian. Just read the letter. It explains everything." Catching his breath, the man went on, "Better wait to read it until you get home, though." Then he smiled at her with warmth that she had seldom felt and looked into her eyes with a knowing that penetrated deep within. Without words, she heard him say within her mind, "God really does love you, Lillian." With that, he turned and walked back between the cars and disappeared among the pedestrians.

"Wait!" Lillian shouted after him. But he was gone.

Lillian shook with adrenalin as she ran her hand over the dented hood and got back into the car. Beth and Evan were chattering, "Who was that man, Mommy? Was he hurt? Will you get put in jail?"

"No kids, he's alright. It was just an accident. These things happen. Buckle up so we can get to soccer practice," she mumbled, starting the car. "Who in heaven's name was that," she asked herself as she glanced at the envelope with her name, "Lillian Frank" written neatly in cursive, sealed and marked "Personal and Confidential."

ಶಿಶಿ ಲಞಲ

Barry Anderson walked through the bedroom door into the kitchen, very pale and very silent. Margaret, the house keeper, looked up at him as she swept the floor.

"What's wrong, Barry, have a bad night?"

Barry just kept walking through the mud room and out the back door, closing it behind him. "No breakfast?" Margaret yelled after him. "He always eats breakfast. What in the world could be wrong with him?"

Barry Anderson was up with the chickens, as always. Of course he didn't have chickens anymore; he raised grains – wheat, barley, some alfalfa, and some cattle. But plowing and planting rousted him out of bed just as early each morning. He enjoyed working in the morning hours before the heat. Now that Elaine was gone he'd usually make his own breakfast on the way out of the house; the housekeeper didn't get paid to cook. Who'd expect he'd lose his wife when he was only 63.

"Men are supposed to go before their women. "God would rather have the men in heaven sooner," he often joked, "Know why? Less talking."! But he missed Elaine terribly. "Married just 40 years," he'd say to himself over and over.

Fortunately his two boys farmed not far off and they worked with Barry now and then. But life just wasn't the same. It seemed like all the joy drained out of him into the casket as they lowered it in the grave. The loneliness felt almost unbearable, like a sharp blade within his gut and a dark curtain over his soul. The boys didn't seem to come around as much and it was all he could do to make himself go to church.

He'd never thought much about widowed folks in church. It has to be the loneliest place on the planet. You come alone, sit alone, and go home alone. He'd considered just staying home on Sundays, tried it a couple of times, and finally just never got around to going back.

Barry wasn't quite in touch with the anger he felt at God for taking Elaine, nor his subconscious attempt to punish God by missing church, yet he knew there was some hidden dark joy in it. But the response from the church sealed his absence. The pastor gave a courtesy phone call to say they missed him, and that was it. His boys asked a few times why he wasn't in church, but Barry felt that down deep nobody really cared anyway. He just responded, "Too busy keeping up the farm all by myself." People seemed to accept the answer and Sunday mornings became a dark time of grief and self-pity.

Work became the only thing that seemed to be satisfying anymore, especially time on the tractor. In the tractor cab you're alone. You can talk to God out loud if you want to. You can cry out loud if you need to. Crying happened a lot lately, but talking to God had seemed to dry up.

If life had been confusing since Elaine's death, today had to be the most confusing day ever. Barry, like Jim and Lillian, had received his own shocking visit. He had been instructed to meet a man, who claimed to be Jesus, on the tractor; this "Jesus" wanted to talk. Didn't matter that the tractor was broken and the part wouldn't be in for another three days. Of course he would never tell anyone!

"Who would believe that someone who claimed to be Jesus Himself appeared to a stark naked man in the shower?"

It happened at exactly 5:30 A.M. on Wednesday, in the farm house. Barry stood washing the sleep off, remembering that there used to be clean towels when Elaine was alive. Suddenly, a man stood at the opening of the shower stall with a towel draped over his arm. Medium build, the man wore blue overalls and a red plaid shirt, with his curly brown hair combed back close like he'd just gotten out of the shower himself.

"Morning, Barry. I'd like to spend some time with you today. Sorry to bother you in the shower, but didn't want to startle you in your sleep, and besides the morning sun will be just right for plowing soon."

Barry bolted back, "What the hell?"

"Not hell, Barry; Heaven! You've been wondering a lot about heaven lately. Wondering about Elaine, wondering if you would ever see her again, wondering if you really believed." Barry stared, frozen in place.

"Meet me on the red tractor in an hour and we will go for a ride," the stranger grinned. He explained the terms of their meeting, got Barry's silent nod, and then disappeared into thin air as the towel fell to the floor.

"Tell anyone?" Barry grumbled as he walked into the barn. "They'd lock me up!"

Chapter 2: Close Encounters

The slow drive to church gave Jim some time to think. As he passed down the clean paved streets lined with small Midwestern middleclass homes, the disturbing events of the night before and the unchanging stability of this little town stood in drastic contradiction. "Emmaus, Nebraska," Jim reflected sarcastically, "isn't much more than the intersection of two roads, one a US highway and the other a State road that connects other nowhere bergs in the Midwest." He remembered flying over the town with a local crop duster and member of his congregation and recalled to himself, "Emmaus looks like a thousand little towns in America – a center crisscross with buildings clustered for a mile or so along each thoroughfare." He'd gotten to know most of the farmers and ranchers that make up the population, as well as the clustered town folk who work as teachers, bankers, cops, shop keepers, and service providers that support the agrarian economy.

Passing the town hall, Jim shook his head and spoke out loud, as if reading from some town history, "Emmaus proudly describes itself as a small town where everyone knows everyone else, for better or worse. If the local newspaper fails to print some happening, the rumor mill will surely 'publish' it— all in graphic detail." Then he paused and mumbled under his breath, "They won't publish this one."

He passed the Lutheran church on the corner and reflected the town's religious history. Emmaus hosts four churches, each one a few blocks from the central crossroads.

The Norwegian and Swedish immigrants formed the Lutheran church; the Dutch planted the Reformed church; mostly Germans make up the Catholic Church, and the strays formed Emmaus Community Church, the newest and furthest from "downtown."

Jim mourned over the changing demographics of church life. "Hell, there was a day when everyone went to church; but not today. Seems like age limits have been imposed on participation—under15 and over 50." He found it strange, though, that the churches still represent a vital part of the community. Vital not because they make a great deal of much practical difference in the life of the town, but because they represent the "American" values embedded in the region's way of life. People love the ethnic jokes, especially the religious ones. Jim couldn't help himself, "One day Ole woke up and saw Jesus standing at the foot of his bed… Great."

Jim smiled at the name of the town, "Emmaus," as he drove past the library. Local folklore mentions something about a traveling Pentecostal preacher who claimed to have seen Jesus, and called the crossroads Emmaus. Jim thought to himself as he pulled into the church parking lot, "It doesn't matter anymore – people just live in Emmaus, live slowly and methodically. Maybe it's the heavy humid air that makes life move so slowly. People don't expect a whole lot, and for good reason; nothing important ever happens."

Returning to last night's events, Jim began to recall the words of the intruder: "Frustrations." Jim had been frustrated all right. He remembered his hopes and dreams in seminary—how he'd build a church that would bring thousands to Christ, a place where people's lives would change and radiate the love of God. He shook his head and wondered, "Just when did those dreams die?" Lately he struggled to keep this little church from simply self-destructing. Pride, opinions, rights, traditions, alliances all seemed so much more real than any work of Jesus. "No wonder the church hasn't grown," he muttered. But Jim knew full well that, somewhere back in the fifteen years he'd served Emmaus his zeal had waned, his sermons had become random biblical expositions, and his leadership had become powerless. "Maybe I should have been the engineer my dad wanted me to be," he sighed.

This last week had really put his stomach in knots. Two factions in the church blamed Jim for declining attendance and tight finances. One afternoon, after a particularly ugly phone call, Jim fell to his knees in his office and called out to God: "Why did You call me to be a pastor if You knew I didn't have what it takes to make it work? Oh God, I really need for You to show up." Now as he pulled into the church parking lot, Pastor James Cline wondered what the day would bring. He frowned. Maybe meeting with Jesus, even if such a thing could happen, wouldn't be so hot. "Doubt I'd hear the old "good and faithful servant" line."

Emmaus Community Church beamed in the morning light like a stone monument to the religious backbone of Elmhurst County. Unlike some of the other "institutions" that called themselves churches, Emmaus prided itself for standing solidly for the Bible. Jim, the seventh pastor in its fifty-three year history, unlocked the empty church building and went in almost cautiously, listening for anything unusual. "Ridiculous!" he said to himself. He walked through the sanctuary which once boasted the largest congregation in the county but now seldom found itself more than half full. Jim passed the chancel and turned down a short hallway to the pastor's study at the rear of the building. On many similar mornings the empty spaces in this proud edifice had seemed to mock him as he'd hurry to his office. The taunts "loser" and "failure" haunted him the most.

Relieved to find nobody there, Jim fixed the coffee, turned up the heat, and started for the Sanctuary for his regular morning devotions. He reached for his Bible and automatically opened it at the red ribbon. "Wait a minute; this isn't where I left off yesterday. Who's been messing with my Bible?" Curiously, Jim looked at the newly marked passage. His

19

forehead furrowed and his eyes stared as he recognized the reference. It was John 14:18-20. Shaken, he read the passage aloud: "I will not leave you as orphans; I will come to you. After a little while the world will no longer see Me, but you will see Me; because I live, you will live also." Jim called his secretary and asked her to take the day off.

Still shaken, Lillian slowly drove the mile to Evan's soccer practice and let him out to join his team. After parking the car, she sat behind the wheel and wept over the near catastrophe. All she needed was another stressor; there were already far more in her life than she could handle. "But thank goodness that man is okay," she muttered. "Walter will be madder than the dickens about that dent in the hood." Her mind returned to the demanding schedule and relationships that exhausted her. Walter traveled with his work all week, leaving Lillian with the household chores, helping with homework, playing taxi mom, and trying to cope with the stress at church. Why in the world she ever let herself get voted onto the Elder Board at Emmaus, she would never know. Each day felt like another hill to climb, only to face another one the next day. Sunday was no different. "What happened to that 'abundant life?" she wondered to herself.

Then her mind returned to the man she'd just hit. In contrast to her shattered nerves, he appeared the epitome of calm. He didn't seem angry that she hit him or worried that he might be hurt, but completely focused on her. Somehow, "abundant life" fit him far more than it did her. Did he really say that God loved her, or did she just think it? She started to open the envelope, but remembered the man's suggestion, "Better wait to read it until you get home."

Just then Evan rushed up and announced that practice had been called due to a chance of lightning. "Let's get home quick," Evan shouted, "so I can play before homework."

"Oh, God, will it never end," Lillian thought to herself.

Returning home, Lillian put the envelope on the kitchen counter and began their late afternoon and evening routine of starting dinner, helping with homework, saying no to hundreds of "Mommy" requests, dinner itself, showers, stories, and kids in bed. Wednesday meant Walt was still on the road, so she had the evening to herself. For hours now the mysterious letter had been calling to her.

With a glass of red wine in hand, she and the letter retired to the couch. A flood of emotions swirled as Lillian started to open the envelope. The thought that it could be a summons of some kind brought dread. Then terror lurked as she considered that maybe the man had been stalking her and that she was in danger. Finally curiosity won as she reflected on the man's gentle spirit and seeming delight in giving her the envelope. A swirling muddle of questions arose. Like the kids just before dinner, the questions all talked at once—about why the man wasn't hurt, what he meant that he'd already been killed for her, that she was so busy this was the only way he could get her attention, and on and on.

Finally, with trembling fingers, she tore loose the seal and removed the neatly hand written note. Lillian read:

Dear Lillian,

I hope that you are not too shaken by today's encounter, but I needed to communicate with you in a way that would get your attention. For months now, you have been pouring your heart out to me and asking me for help and advice, but you end your prayers before listening to my response. I know how exhausted and frustrated you are, how unfulfilled you feel in your marriage, with Walter traveling so much. Believe it or not, I do understand what it is like to parent young children. I am so glad that you accepted my invitation to serve in your church, but you need to let me guide you. I know you feel so trapped by all that's going on and you've begun to wonder if I would really help you. I have spoken to you in a dozen ways, Lillian, through the Scriptures you've read, your pastor's sermons, the hymns at church, through Walt's suggestions, through whispers during the day, and even billboards with "Jesus loves you," on them. But you have just been too busy to listen. I think you have given up hope that I would really speak to you. Every time you called out "Jesus," I was right there.

So, Lillian, I would like to suggest that we meet personally, in circumstances a little more conducive to conversation than the car incident this afternoon. I would like you to meet me at the Corner Coffee Shop tomorrow morning, at 10:00 AM, after your hair appointment.

I have one condition, however. You may never tell anyone about the incident this morning, this letter, my request, or about meeting with me. If you attempt to tell anyone about this, I will immediately erase the memory of the whole encounter and you will never recall any of it. To help you keep our confidence, I will make this letter disappear before morning.

Lillian, I hope you will trust me and come and meet me tomorrow. The Father, the Spirit, and I really do love you and want to help.

Jesus

Lillian sat and stared at the letter for what seemed like hours. Every question, every doubt, every fear possible went through her mind. But it was true: The writer of the letter knew about the events earlier that day, and had, in fact, written about them before they happened. He knew what she'd been praying about and how she felt about life. He knew things that she'd not shared with anyone. If God wanted her attention, He sure had it. Lillian got up and locked the letter in the family safe so it wouldn't be seen, and went to bed hoping to sleep. "If this is real, it could change everything," she thought. Sleep came surprisingly quickly.

છબછબ પછપછ

The morning sun bathed Emmaus Community Church, warming its large reddish stones chiseled from the local quarry. Yellow sunbeams blazed through the stain glass windows, each pane placed in honor of one of the founding members. This Wednesday the church was empty, except for the pastor who sat alone in the sanctuary. For fifteen years it had been his practice to spend his first hour of the day in the second pew on the east side where the sun first peeked in. Bible in hand, he would read a chapter or two, pray through the intercession list for the congregation, and mull over the day ahead.

Today his Bible, now lying on the pew, sat open to John 14, the Intercessory Prayer list still lay on his desk in the church office. Jim stared at the large brass cross behind the choir loft in the front of the sanctuary, wondering what the day would bring. Seven hours remained before someone claiming to be Jesus promised to show up in his office. "Dear Lord," Jim started, and then his words trailed off. What could he say? Thoughts and feelings swirled inside him. He felt excited and terrified at the same time; encircling the two feelings a terrible skepticism filled his heart like smoke from a smoldering garbage fire. Jim mumbled, "God just doesn't do things like this. The appearances of Jesus stopped with the Ascension. If this is some sort of elaborate hoax, it has to be the most ridiculous, even cruel, thing a person could do."

It would be cruel because Jim wanted it to be true with all his heart. He'd always felt that Jesus eluded him, hidden just behind the pages of his theology books, or disguised in coincidental answers to prayer—and so silent. Jim never wanted merely a theological or religious relationship with Jesus, but something more personal. In the early days after Jim's conversion, God seemed so real, so active, so powerful, even if hidden. But as the years of ministry wore on, Jesus seemed to withdraw into the pages of the Bible, to be proclaimed, interpreted, defended, but never really experienced. Jim would encourage himself with the verse from Hebrews, "Now faith is the assurance of things hoped for, the conviction of things not seen." The passage, frustratingly, went on to recall biblical people who actually experienced God in some tangible way, and Jim wasn't sure he ever had, at least not for a long time. Quite the reverse, the more he prayed about the troubles at church, the worse things seemed to get. "Forgive my lack of faith, Lord. I know I'm angry and even bitter. Why would You want to appear to me? Maybe I'm in more trouble than I thought!"

After returning to his office, Jim tried to organize the calendar for the week and work on his message for Sunday, but he simply couldn't concentrate. He called Kate twice just to see if anything new was going on at home. Finally he decided to check email, then go to lunch, make a few hospital calls, and be back at the office by 3:45pm. On his way out, he made sure that the office door and the front church door were locked. If this was some sort of joke, he wasn't going to make it easy.

Pastor Jim returned to church just before 3:45 PM, locked the front door after him, and went straight to his office. As he unlocked the office door and walked into the small cluttered room, he was startled to see a smiling man sitting in one of the counseling chairs.

"Right on time," the man said. Standing, he put out his hand, "Hi, my name is Jesus of Nazareth. I am so glad we have this time, Jim. Sit down."

Jim sat down and stared. The man across from him seemed a bit younger than Jim, medium build, curly dark brown hair, short beard, and brilliant brown-green eyes. Wearing Dockers and a casual shirt, the visitor appeared at the same time the most intense and the most harmless man he'd ever met. His warm smile seemed to be directed not only "at" Jim, but "within him."

Jim stared dumb founded. Although he usually did all the talking during his prayer times, Jim had nothing to say now that Jesus appeared to be sitting across the small office from him. As if not wanting to impose an uncomfortable silence, the visitor began, "I know, Jim, this is really hard to believe, but I do want you to be able to feel confident that I really am who I say I am."

He showed Jim deep scars in his hands and pulled up his shirt tails revealing a long angular scar on the right side of his abdomen. He went on to describe, in detail, some of Jim's most recent prayers, prayers that he hadn't even shared with Kate. Jim leaned forward in his chair as the man went on, "I love you, Jim. I want to help you." His voice was deep and rich, full of warmth and love. As he spoke, Jim not only heard the words, but felt them like a warm vibration somewhere in his chest.

"I, I don't know what to say," Jim responded.

"You don't have to say anything, Jim. There will be lots of time for saying things and asking things. However, I would like to share some thoughts with you."

Jesus talked for about half an hour. He told Jim that his prayers have been heard and that He and the Father want to help him. "But there is so much you have to learn, Jim—truths you heard in Sunday school and again in Seminary. Trouble is, you haven't taken much of it seriously—so far, that is. Most importantly you need to remember what I underlined in your Bible. "I will not leave you as orphans; I will come to you." I am here, with you, Jim, now, all the time, loving you, forgiving you, trying to lead you." Jesus seemed to almost plead.

Jim remained speechless, yet his mind raced. Of course he knew that God is present with us—"omnipresent" the textbooks say. Yet Jim realized that when he prayed, he bowed his head as if there was no one present with him. He directed his prayers somewhere out there or up there to wherever heaven resides. When Jim finished praying what he wanted to pray, he said amen, and got up and left, as if the prayers would take some time to travel to wherever Jesus lived and the answers would also take some time to get back. Maybe Jesus is present, has been present; but that's not the way Jim felt or acted.

The strange visitor went on, "I would like to schedule several get-togethers like this. I'll still be around the rest of the time, of course, but I think you'll find it helpful if we can see each other for a few more times. Remember though, not a word. I'll meet with you in your office next Wednesday, at the same time."

Jim caught himself just before he blurted out that he already had an appointment on Wednesday at that time and would he mind fitting into another time slot. "I'll be here," Jim responded cautiously. Jim stood as the man started toward the door. Then he stopped and turned toward Jim.

"Are you up for a hug, Jim?" He asked, smiling. To Jim's surprise, he felt himself withdraw slightly. "That's okay, maybe another day," The visitor smiled and turned the corner. "I'll let myself out," He said as he disappeared down the hallway.

৪৩৪৩ ৫৩৫৩

"Well, I'll be…" Barry mumbled, when he heard the red tractor purring in the equipment barn. As he approached the tractor Barry could see two figures sitting in the cab, one man-sized and the other smaller. Barry stood on the ground and stared up. The man shouted down, "Come on up! Let's go for a ride!"

Barry climbed the ladder and leaned into the large tractor cab, outfitted with air conditioning, stereo, power steering, and two-way radio. He stared first at the man wearing the same overalls he'd seen earlier that morning. Barry noticed his short wavy dark brown hair and a short beard that accented his solid jaw, prominent nose, and shining smile. His strong hand reached down and pulled Barry into the passenger seat, which strangely seemed big enough to hold both of them. But before Barry could start asking questions, he stared with amazement at the boy seated behind the wheel of the tractor. He couldn't have been more than six years old with blond fluffy hair, freckles on his nose, and a wide smile.

"Who's that?" Barry grumbled.

"That's Johnny," the man responded, "He was killed by a tractor like this one a few years ago, and I'm helping him get past his fear. I thought he could drive while you and I talk."

"Killed?" Barry responded wide-eyed. Then he caught sight of the man's eyes, eyes he'd been too distracted to see in the shower, too shocked to notice when he climbed into the cab. The man's large eyes seemed like windows into an eternity of lush green fields. Deep, smiling, knowing, loving, forgiving—they probed deep into Barry's heart and spoke to him without words, the kind of encounter Barry had only experienced in prayer. He felt loved and known, as though he were standing, or sitting, on holy ground.

Barry exclaimed. "No shit!" without knowing what he was saying. "I mean… it's really You!"

Then Johnny drove the tractor out of the shed and rolled out into the field where he plowed perfect furrows, back and forth. "I ain't much for words," Barry said finally.

"No need. Let's just ride awhile." Jesus settled back and enjoyed the ride, with an occasional comment about the soil or

27

the amount of moisture. But for the most part, the three plowed silently for the next hour or so. Barry could have spent the rest of his life right there in that tractor, plowing.

ഩഩ ൧൧

Lillian's hair appointment felt like a blur. A perm and a cut seemed pretty simple; why did Sally have to chatter on so? Lillian had to think. "Maybe I should call the police. What if this guy is some sort of weirdo who wants to kidnap me? Right. Just tell the police that you hit a man on the road yesterday and then left without reporting it because he might have been a stalker. Yeah, right." At first, the time dragged on but now she felt afraid she'd be late. "Sally, I really do have an appointment."

"Who with?" Sally responded, expecting to know about everything that happened in their small town.

"Church stuff," Lillian answered shortly, getting out of the chair.

The Corner Coffee Shop was only a half mile from Sally's Salon, but it felt like a cross country drive. "This traffic light has got to be broken," she fussed. Lillian parked discretely down the street from the coffee shop—maybe she'd seen too many spy movies—and walked the rest of the way. The Corner Coffee Shop, usually busy this time of day, looked deserted except for the waitress and a lone man sitting in the far booth. It was the man she'd hit with the car yesterday, the man who'd given her the letter.

Lillian walked slowly toward the back booth. As she approached, she surveyed this amazingly plain but handsome young man, with curly dark brown hair, short beard, and the most amazing greenish-brown eyes. The eyes themselves smiled as if they not only liked her, but liked what was within her. Heavy eyebrows accented his prominent nose and tanned youthful face. He reached out his strong scarred hand, "Hello Lillian, I am your friend, Jesus. Please sit down."

Lillian took her seat, but unlike Jim, was not speechless. "Come on, you can't expect me to believe that…."

Jesus interrupted, "I know. That's been the problem all along. So many people have let you down over the years that you find it hard to believe in anyone, even me." Jesus went on to list the people that Lillian felt had always let her down, starting with her father and mother, siblings, teachers, and finally even her husband, Walter. "That's why I want to meet with you like this, face to face, to help you believe that I love you and that I am always with you. I will never leave you or forsake you." Jesus paused and then went on, "Remember the Samaritan woman that I met by Jacob's well? She told the villagers that she believed in me when I told her things that only God could know. I spoke to her about what lay in her heart. Look within your heart, Lillian, and you'll know that I'm your Lord." Jesus waited.

Lillian felt that the universe had suddenly gone silent, as if there were only two people on the whole globe, two people talking in the Emmaus Corner Coffee Shop—everyone else, everything else held its breath. Time had stopped and Jesus waited.

"I want to believe that You're really Jesus," Lillian whispered. "I want to believe that Jesus loves me enough to appear to me like this." She paused. "But this couldn't happen to me; maybe only to really holy people. If You're who you say You are, You know what I'm like inside. Maybe the Samaritan woman's not such a bad comparison."

"Maybe not," Jesus smiled. "But don't worry; believing is a choice we have to make each day, each minute. There's time." Jesus paused and then went on, "Meanwhile, I would like for us to keep meeting. Next time, however, let's meet in your family room—5:30 A.M, before your day gets going. Thursday."

Just then the waitress interrupted, "Something to eat, ma'am?" Lillian looked up, turned her head to see the waitress, and then glanced to where Jesus had been sitting.

"No thanks, I already have a lot to chew on." When she returned home Lillian went right to the safe, to reread the letter. She discovered, however, it had vanished. Later that day she noticed the dent in the car hood had disappeared, as well.

Chapter 3: Discovering Love

The following week Jim felt as though someone had moved every piece of furniture in the house of his life. The daily routine that had provided stability to his world now seemed meaningless. The next Wednesday, when he planned to meet Jesus, loomed over every moment like a giant meteor streaking toward earth, threatening its very existence. "What in God's name is going …?" He caught himself in mid-sentence. "God's name. How casually I use that phrase."

Although Jim had earnestly pleaded with God in prayer to do something that would relieve his misery at church, he never actually expected Jesus to do anything – certainly nothing like this. Everything had its place. Jim's was here, working as a husband, father, and pastor. Jesus' place should be at the right hand of God, looking down and occasionally helping with the long finger of the Holy Spirit. Now that Jesus showed up here, it seemed that the whole universe, from Jim's perspective, had been turned on its edge.

Would the man who called Himself Jesus appear again next Wednesday? Jim desperately wanted Him to be there, but at the same time felt terrified at the thought. "He seemed nice enough," Jim reflected. But as soon as that thought had settled in, another more startling thought pushed it out of his head. "Jesus doesn't just show up to chit chat. When Jesus met with biblical characters, their lives were turned totally upside down. In the end, most of them got themselves killed over it." Jim winced. Dread gripped his heart and yet next Wednesday's meeting felt like the doorway to the rest of his life. "Why did He have to wait a week? Couldn't He just get it over with right then and there? Why stretch this out and make me suffer?" Every minute of the following days felt like a whole day in itself; sleep became almost nonexistent. Jim prayed, "Lord, if this is really You, please give me the courage to survive this week."

Wednesday finally arrived, finding Jim sitting in his office alone an hour or so before his appointment with Jesus. Again, he'd given his secretary, Susan, the day off, but he wasn't at all sure that the man, who claimed to be Jesus, would come again. Jim sat in one of the counseling chairs reflecting. With knots in his stomach and shoulder muscles just as tied up, he put his face in his hands in silent prayer. When he looked up, the man was sitting across from him.

"Good afternoon, Jim. I'm sorry this week has been so rough for you." He grinned and then sat silently for a few minutes.

Jim just stared and absorbed the sight before him. It was the same man, all right, but in the previous two encounters Jim hadn't really studied Him. Dressed again in tan Dockers and a sport shirt open at the collar, He appeared quite ordinary. But as Jim studied His face and eyes, he saw at the same time a beautiful youthfulness and a maturity that could have made Him thousands of years old. Jesus looked slender and shorter than most men today, but he appeared to be in perfect physical shape. "What does the Son of God do to stay fit just sitting on a throne all day?" Jim wondered before he could catch himself.

"Eat right and get plenty of exercise," Jesus answered Jim's thought with a laugh. "The throne isn't really a chair, Jim, but a place, and being Creator and Redeemer and Life for all of creation keeps Us on the move." Before the picture had time to fully form in Jim's mind, Jesus went on. "Jim, how would you like me to help you?"

The question caught Jim off guard. It felt like a question whose answer would take a lifetime. He had a thousand questions to ask Jesus. What he needed now seemed little more than irrelevant. "You know everything; You know what I need," Jim finally responded.

"I know far more about what you need than you could ever guess. But I want us to begin with what you know, with the things on your mind." Jesus waited as Jim thought.

Jim reflected with caution because it appeared that this man could understand his thoughts. The question made him feel as though he had just won the lottery and someone had asked him how he wanted to spend it. "How can God help a person?" he thought. "What <u>couldn't</u> He help me with? Where would I even start to answer such a question?"

Jesus interrupted, "Why don't you start with what you have been praying about lately?"

"Well, you've supposedly heard all that. Do You really want me to go through it again?"

"You'll find it helpful to say it to me in person. When you talked with me before, you weren't sure anyone was listening. But now here we are, so let's just talk together like men."

Jim didn't know where to begin, but just blurted out the first thing that came to mind. "Things at church aren't going so well. The congregation isn't growing and we're struggling financially. Worst of all, factions fight about how to fix things."

"What, in all that, bothers you the most, Jim?"

Jim stared at Jesus, knowing that He was asking about his heart, not the church. "I'm discouraged, I guess. I feel like a failure. My dreams about doing something great for the Kingdom—ah, seem so hopeless, like pieces of paper that have been scattered by a huge windstorm. I feel trapped. No matter what I do, nothing seems to change. I'm not the husband or father I should be; my mind is so distracted." Jim paused. "'Trapped' says it I guess." He concluded, "Maybe You need to find me another job where I can succeed—maybe call a different pastor for this church."

By now, tears were streaming down Jim's face. He'd grappled with this pain before, but never in its entirety like he did right now. He felt as though Jesus was the Judge sitting on the throne, and he was hearing the word "Guilty!" coming from a jury of the hosts of heaven. He began to sob with his face in his hands. Suddenly, he felt a hand on his shoulder.

"Jim, I think you need that hug right now. Stand up."

Jim obeyed as Jesus pulled him to his feet and threw both arms around him. Jim just stood motionless without returning the embrace. He didn't feel worthy to return it, to put his arms around the Son of God. Nevertheless, Jesus held him close, and it felt to Jim as though all of heaven was holding him, loving him, forgiving him. He felt absorbed in the embrace, and his pain and self-incrimination seemed to flow into Jesus and beyond Him, not as though it disappeared, but as if the pain became held and experienced by all the heavenly hosts. Jim found his face against Jesus' skin, his tears wet between their cheeks. Jesus held him silently for what seemed like an eternity as Jim finally relaxed. He not only didn't feel alone, but he rested in the embrace with a Peace he had never experienced before.

Jesus gradually released His grip and looked Jim in the face with a warm smile, and the two men returned to their chairs. "Thank you for sharing your heart with me, Jim."

Jim looked up at Jesus and saw that tears were flowing from Jesus' eyes as well.

"I love you, Jim. I'm in this with you. You're here at Emmaus because I called you to pastor these people. You can do what I want done here, and I am with you to help you do it. But we're meeting together about much more than this church and its success. It's about you, Jim. It's about you growing and becoming the beautiful person you really are. That becoming happens even in this pain you're experiencing, but you have to trust me to guide you through it."

Jim sat and stared at Jesus for a long time and then responded, "I want to, Lord; I really do."

"Let's meet again next week at the same time. Meanwhile, remember that I'm with you even though you can't see or hear me. When you need my strength or wisdom, the Holy Spirit will be there to give it to you. He lives in you, you know." Jesus smiled and turned toward the door.

Jim jumped to his feet and asked, "May I have another hug?" Before Jesus could respond, Jim reached out and grasped Him with both arms and pulled Jesus to his chest. Jesus' arms embraced and held him. Soon, Jim relaxed his grip and the two men stepped apart. This time, Jim was smiling as well.

"You'll see me here next week," Jesus said as He turned and walked down the hall. Calling back over his shoulder, Jesus added, "And remember, I am with you always!"

ജ്ഞ ൬൬

Like Jim, Lillian survived the next week in a haze. She simply could not get the encounter with the man in the cafe out of her mind. Worse, she couldn't talk to anyone about it. Normally, she would discuss stressful or confusing issues with Walt or one of her friends from church, but in this case, that was impossible. It was all she could do not to approach Pastor Jim after church and ask him some oblique questions about whether or not Jesus appears to people in our time. Then she realized he would want to know why she was asking and so decided not to say anything. Finally Thursday arrived and Lillian awoke at 12:01AM. Sleep had been almost impossible. Normally she would be up by 5:30 AM, the appointed meeting time, but not yet showered, dressed, with makeup on. By 3:30 AM, however, she sat on the couch in the family room, ready for whatever might happen, if anything. If He came, she hoped the doorbell wouldn't wake up the kids.

Morning light had just begun to give definition to the light fluffy clouds and the plants and trees in the dew-covered yard. The robins had already started their breakfast trek around the flower beds, calling back and forth with news of a find here and there. The Frank home sat silently awaiting the 7:00 AM alarm set for the kids to get ready for school.

At exactly 5:30 AM, Lillian was startled by a hand on her shoulder. She lifted her head from the couch pillow where she had slumped over asleep an hour or so earlier. She jumped to her feet. "I didn't hear the doorbell," she stammered.

"Didn't want to wake up the kids. I hear you make a great cup of coffee. Just black for me, thanks."

"I set the timer for 5:15 AM; I'll go see if it's ready. Do you want to join me in the kitchen?"

Jesus followed Lillian into the kitchen as she filled the cups she had already set out. They walked back into the family room where Lillian nervously looked around wondering where to sit. "The two recliners felt too far away; sitting together on the couch felt too close...."

"Why don't you sit on the end of the couch and I'll take the recliner," Jesus suggested. They took their places and sipped the fresh coffee in silence.

While Jesus seemed content to sit and enjoy the coffee, Lillian's mind raced: "This would feel much more like a visitation from Jesus if he wore a white robe or something. Jeans and a sport shirt just doesn't fit what I'd pictured. Who does his ironing? I wouldn't have picked that shirt to go with his eyes...." Slowly, her attention turned again to Jesus' features. His hair looked like it had been brushed into place with his hands—casual and flowing. His beard looked nicely trimmed. "I wonder if His mother gives him advice on how to dress," then scolded herself, "Men hate that..." then rethought that Jesus probably wouldn't mind because His ego wouldn't be so fragile. "He seems so comfortable, so sure of Himself, so in control—certainly not like someone pretending to be Jesus." Thoughts seemed to crowd into the previous ones, pushing them out of her mind before they fully formed.

Finally, Jesus broke the whirlwind of random thoughts, "Lillian, I know you've been thinking a lot this week about our meeting, wondering if I really am who I say I am.

Despite any proof I could have given you, I think you'll find that you already do believe I'm genuine. It's there in your heart."

Lillian reflected silently for a few moments, as if leaving the family room and walking into her heart to search for some hidden truth. "You're right. Despite doubts and questions, I do have a sense that You really are Jesus."

"The Holy Spirit told you that the first day we met, Lillian, but it sometimes takes a while before folks realize that He's spoken or decide to believe what He says. I had to learn to listen to Him myself."

"So why are You here—in this way, I mean? I've never heard about You appearing physically since biblical times. Of course, with the promise You swore me to, it could be happening all the time and I'd never hear about it. But that still doesn't explain why You're appearing to me."

"You're right, Lillian, it doesn't explain. I'm here for a number of reasons, most of which fall way beyond explaining. But I can tell you that I made myself known to you because I love you and because you asked me to help you. Beyond that, I can only say that you'll come to understand some of my purposes as they unfold in the months and years ahead. But right now, tell me how you'd like me to help you."

Again the whirlwind of thoughts flooded Lillian's mind: marriage, kids, church, how she felt about herself, Walter…. She pulled out of the muddle and responded, "I don't know where to start; there are so many things. Maybe if I took some time to think about it, I could give a better answer."

"Take your time. Evan and Beth won't wake up for another hour or so." Jesus sipped His coffee and waited.

Finally, Lillian turned and faced Jesus. "I need You to help me believe that You really do love me—personally I mean—myself, as ungrateful and mixed up as I feel most of the time. I read the passages in the Bible about what a good Christian should be like—you know—patient, kind, loving, and so on. I may look okay to others from the outside, but from within here there's a lot to be desired. You must be constantly disappointed with me; I certainly am with myself."

"If I expected you to be perfect, Lillian, I would have made you an angel." Jesus waved His hands around in the air, as if pointing and smiling at some unseen beings in the room. "You and all humankind struggle with the sickness of sin. That's why I came in the Bethlehem manger and to Jerusalem and the cross, and here, now, in your family room. Sin needn't separate us anymore, Lillian. My Father and I forgive you. We love you and want you to be free to live a life of love. I desire love in your heart, not perfection."

Lillian teared up. She had heard of unconditional love, but until now, sitting in her family room, she had never quite believed it. But here He sat, looking at her with a depth of tenderness she had never experienced before. For the first time since she came to believe in Jesus, she realized that love and forgiveness were not mere theological concepts, but the very nature of a real Person.

"I guess I'd like You to teach me how to live my life in freedom and love. Lately, I've felt anything but freedom. Every minute of every day seems owed to someone, even You. It's not that I don't love Walter and the kids and my friends, and You, but it doesn't feel like freedom to me. Sometimes I resent all the demands, and that doesn't feel like love either."

Jesus listened as if to let Lillian's words float in the space between them and then allow them to come together, settling on the table, like a figurine that they could both consider. Finally Jesus responded, "I know what it's like to have people want every second of your time and energy and never to give you any rest. It's hard work. It's hard to find space for yourself. I couldn't have done it without My Father's help. Would it be all right if I helped you, Lillian? That's what it means to follow me; to let me lead you and give you strength. When you let me do that, joy comes—a wonderful joy."

"I always thought that following You meant just to stick to the right beliefs and to obey biblical principles. It feels better to follow You as a Person. But I'm afraid that I don't know how—that is, in a day-to-day way."

"That's what I came to show you, Lillian. There's so much I am looking forward to teaching you. I think you'll find it fun." Jesus' eyes twinkled and a broad smile reflected His anticipation. "If you want to continue, let's meet again next Thursday morning, and maybe a few beyond that." Jesus stood and faced Lillian. He reached out His scarred hand as Lillian received it in hers. "Remember the bottom line, Lillian—I always love you. No matter how you're feeling about yourself or how others seem to feel about you, I love you. You are precious to me."

Lillian stared into Jesus' eyes and felt, deep within her, that Truth had spoken. His words created a confidence that could never be erased. "I'd very much like to meet again," she whispered, just as Beth's voice rang out from the bedroom. "Mommy."

ജ്ഞ രൂര

As He did with Jim and Lillian, Jesus had suggested that He and Barry meet again the next week. "We have a lot to talk about, Barry. Meet you next week at the same time, but in the barn this time; it's going to rain pretty hard that day." Without even giving Barry a chance to respond, Jesus had grabbed Johnny's hand and the two skipped around the side of the barn and disappeared.

It wouldn't be an exaggeration to say that Barry thought of nothing but Jesus for the entire next week. Part of Barry actively dreaded the next meeting. When God says that "we have a lot to talk about," it can't be good. "How many people mess up so badly that Jesus has to make a personal call?" he wondered.

Yet the tractor ride with Jesus had really been quite amazing. First, Barry realized that he had absolutely no doubt about the identity of his visitor. When a man spends hours alone on a tractor or combine he gets pretty well acquainted with his own heart. What he thinks and believes doesn't get as muddled up as it does in the midst of city life. When he just sits with a man for hours, without a word, he comes to know something about him, too. Barry watched Jesus' attentiveness to Johnny and His obvious pride at how well Johnny conquered his fear. As the boy plowed with a swirl technique, Jesus laughed out loud, clapped and shouted praises over Johnny. Johnny beamed, and the love between them felt like warm sunlight filling the tractor cab. Barry noticed how Jesus sat back in the tractor seat, totally relaxed and comfortable with Himself. He observed as Jesus would watch the soil turn over in furrows, rich and ready for the next crop. Once, when they spotted a fox slipping under the fence and heading toward the next field, Jesus blew a kiss. The fox stopped and turned. Barry wondered if it would run up and want to sit on Jesus' lap.

Time alone to reflect seemed to fill that week. More plowing, long drives to the feed store, walks to check the cows—all felt like living in a movie theater, re-watching the events of that one day. Barry studied the screen in his head and saw, in that one Man, love, joy, peace, patience, kindness, goodness, gentleness, faithfulness, and self-control. At the same time, he sensed an amazing strength of body, mind, and soul. Barry tried to piece it all together in his mind. "He's completely alive," Barry exclaimed to himself.

After a fitful night, Barry hit the shower again at 5:30 AM, thankful that Jesus had said to meet in the barn instead of the bathroom. Following a quick breakfast of coffee, cereal and toast, Barry dashed through the rain to the barn. The smell of hay, old wood, and tool oil invited Barry even more powerfully than the magnetic aroma of warm bread that Elaine used to bake. "The barn is a man's world," Barry thought. "I wonder if He's here."

Just then a voice rang out from the hayloft above, "Morning, Barry." Brown hair littered with hay appeared over the edge, followed by laughing eyes and then a man sailing through the air, landing a couple of feet in front of him. "I love barns," Jesus sang as he twirled around, as if showing off the surroundings. "Great to be able to meet again, Barry. Let's sit over here on the hay." Barry sat uneasily on the edge of one bale while Jesus leapt into the air like a kid and landed with a thud next to Barry and leaned against the haystack.

Barry spoke up, "Thanks for the wonderful time in the tractor last week. I really appreciated it; it changed me somehow. But I'm confused. Why are You appearing to me like this? What do You want to talk about? Mad at me for not going to church? Is something terrible going to happen?"

Jesus looked at Barry with a soft knowing that made him feel more naked than he had been in the shower. "Things aren't terrible when I am here, Barry, no matter what happens," Jesus smiled as His right eyebrow lifted. "Barry, you're one of the knights in my Kingdom, you know. I love you and I've come to enlist your help."

Barry's jaw dropped with disbelief and surprise. "Knights?" Jesus waited as the words took root. Barry went on, "I'm not sure what that means, and I know You don't make mistakes, but it sure sounds like one to me. I'm sure nothing special." Then another pause, "Does that mean I'm about to die?"

Jesus leaned forward and grabbed Barry by both shoulders, "Not yet, Barry. You see, my Kingdom exists here and now as well as in heaven. 'Thy kingdom come' in the Lord's Prayer refers to an ongoing process; it began when I was born on earth and continues until the day when I return in glory. When you believed in me you became my Father's son, my brother. I'm your King, and you're my knight. It's been that way for a long time."

"I sure don't feel like any knight."

"Let me help you put all this into context, Barry. Take my hand and let's do some remembering." Jesus took Barry's hand, clasping it in both of His. "Just relax." Barry did relax and in an instant he and Jesus were traveling through time.

41

Unlike the flat movie screen that had played in Barry's head all week, he and Jesus seemed present simultaneously in the times Barry remembered and many that he hadn't. Beginning with his mother's womb and its stillness, they traveled through the pain and dazzling brightness of Barry's birth. Together they watched him grow up as a young boy; they listened to the Bible stories that accompanied each bedtime. Days at school, learning to drive the tractor, evenings alone in his room after being punished, playing with his friends in the nearby forest— all flew past. Every detail was revealed as though in high-speed Technicolor.

They watched as Barry, a teenager went forward in church and gave his heart to God. They walked down the aisle together with Barry and Elaine at their wedding and stood and watched the birth of their boys. The years flashed by, ending abruptly with Elaine's funeral seemingly frozen in time. Barry just stood and stared. When the visions stopped, Barry pondered, as if he'd been lagging behind, still at the grave. After a long pause, he responded.

"Got sidetracked, didn't I?"

"A little bit, Barry. But I am here to help you with that if you'll let me. I know this is hard to believe, but the best still awaits you. Can you see how your entire life has been preparing you for something yet to come? The story isn't over, is it?"

"I'm a little frightened," Barry responded.

Chapter 4: Uncomfortable Conversations

Jesus continued to meet individually each week with Jim, Lillian, and Barry. In those conversations, Jesus progressively engaged each one in two basic themes: first forgiveness and then abundant life. Each conversation focused deeply and personally in ways that exposed the inner turmoil and misunderstanding that had stalled their relationships with God.

Jesus said to Barry one day, "Barry, I'd like to talk to you about forgiveness."

"What about forgiveness?" Barry responded a little defensively.

"You think I have a grudge against you and I know you've got one against me. We need to talk about forgiveness."

Barry began to sweat under his woolen shirt. As he heard the word "forgiveness," the word "sin" flashed like a red neon sign in his mind. "I know I've screwed up a lot. My list is too long to go through, and You know it already. I've tried to do better, even to go back to church, but it doesn't seem like much has changed. I know I've got a temper, want things my own way...."

Jesus interrupted what was to become a long self-condemning tirade and said, "I know the list, Barry. The list isn't the real problem; it's what you and I are going to do about it." Barry perspired even more profusely.

Jesus raised the subject of forgiveness with Jim by saying, "Jim, you and I both feel a barrier between us, something that keeps you from letting me really get close to you."

Jim sat silently for a few minutes and then looked at Jesus as tears welled up in his eyes. In a rare use of off-color language, he said, "Shit. Lord, I feel like shit. I know what my life is supposed to look like. I know what the Bible says about a pure heart, and I know that mine stinks like manure. Preaching about holiness only fans the fumes of what I smell like inside. I try; I really do, but I don't get any better. It feels hopeless."

Jesus listened unemotionally and responded, "Why do you think that puts a barrier between us, Jim?"

"Because I hate the way I think and feel and sometimes respond to others, and I know You must hate it even more! I want to be close to You, but how can I? I despise who I am and when I think about it, with You in mind, I feel even worse."

"Then a safe distance from me feels better to you?"

"Yes—I mean no. It does feel that way, but I don't want it to. I know about the cross and Your forgiveness, but…."

Jesus raised his eyebrows and responded, "Knowing about it and knowing it are two different things, Jim."

ಬಾಹಾ ಎಂಎ

In the early morning hours of Lillian's family room the first rays of the sun brightened the corner of an otherwise unlit room. Jesus sat in his accustomed place on the couch and Lillian in her chair. The sunlight went unnoticed as her head hung in shame. She had broached the subject about sin with Jesus and now crumbled under the full weight of her self-condemnation. "I've felt like a bad person all my life, Lord. I know that You forgive my sins, but it doesn't seem to change how I feel about myself. If I were truly repentant, I would change my behavior, my thoughts, and my selfishness. I know I am not going to hell for my sins, but when I see what's really inside me, I feel like hell has come here!"

Jesus responded softly, "Lillian, what do you want me to do?"

"I need You to help me get beyond this. There has to be more to life than pretending I am doing fine, realizing that I'm messing it up, repenting, feeling better, and then starting the whole cycle over again!" She paused, then lifted her head and whispered in exasperation, "What happened to abundant life?"

Jesus sat quietly for a few minutes and then responded lovingly, "You're on the right track, Lillian. But before we can get to abundant life, we need to deal with this forgiveness issue."

ဆဝ‌ဆ ‌ဈ‌ဈ

Each of the three struggled to really accept, deep down in their hearts, that Jesus truly forgave them. They had judged themselves when they sinned and then projected that same judgment onto God.

Jesus said to each of them in pretty much the same way, "I know this is hard to understand, but way before you were born, I knew you. As I hung there on the cross, I reached out through time and space and received all your sins upon myself. I broke the power of sin and death to control your life. The Father and I forgave you and offered the Holy Spirit to give you resurrection power to live in a new way. You therefore have to change the way you look at sin. You see, I changed the consequences of your sins from judgment and condemnation to opportunities for growth and healing. It's not that sin is unimportant, not at all. Sin ruins your life and keeps you from fully knowing me. But when we look at your sins through the lens of my cross and resurrection, we see a mirror image of the

45

potential opposite quality, the character you've been given as the Father's child, my disciple, my beloved.

When you see selfishness, for example, don't be discouraged, but rejoice that your real quality—the opposite of selfishness, love for others, wants to emerge. You just have to cooperate with me as we gradually create a new heart that can love and live the way you were meant to. The Holy Spirit reveals your sins, not to make you feel guilty, but to make you want to be different—to become the "real" you. Repentance shouldn't be self-flagellation, but turning to me with a deep desire for me to develop the opposite quality in you."

Jesus continued, "Another way to look at sin relates to the First Commandment: 'You shall not have any other gods before Me.' You were meant to live your life in sync with Us, trusting in Our wisdom, power, and love, to add Our attributes to your own. But you and most others have depended on created things for your wisdom, power, and affirmation. As those things let you down, the Holy Spirit calls you to let go of them and place those same needs in me. It takes a long time for most of my followers to learn to do that. That 'long time' causes them and others a lot of pain."

Jim, Lillian, and Barry knew about that pain, both for themselves and others. Strangely they had used that pain to turn away from God and His help rather than to draw closer to Him. Sweet times emerged as each one sat with open hearts before Jesus, letting the review of their lives unfold, receiving His forgiveness, love, and healing.

Jesus addressed another dimension of forgiveness, reflected in His earlier conversation with Barry, when He said, "…You think I have a grudge against you and I know you've got one against me." Jesus lovingly confronted Barry about accusing God of killing his wife. He also showed Jim how he blamed God for the failures at church or at least for getting him into such a mess.

Lillian, however, raised the issue before Jesus brought it up. "Please forgive me for blaming You for my failings. I didn't have the courage to tell Walt that I needed him home more, so I prayed that You would make him stay home. When my kids acted their age, I grumbled and complained rather than thanking You for giving them to me. Yet I don't know what I'd do without Walt or my kids. I blamed You because church wasn't this perfect and spiritually encouraging place and I begrudged having to put up with the "imperfections" of others. Rather than seeing my own sin, I've tried to make You out to be the bad guy. I've accused You of failing me when I should have recognized my own failure and asked for forgiveness and help."

Jesus stood up and walked to Lillian and raised her to her feet. He looked into her eyes and smiled, "I am used to people accusing me for everything that goes wrong, Lillian. I forgive you and I love you."

Lillian buried her face in Jesus' shoulder and wept.

℘℘ ℭℛ

Barry and Jim weren't so easily softened, however. "You could have healed her," Barry almost shouted.

Jim responded more subtly. "You called me to this church, knowing my weaknesses. I thought You would make it work and accomplish the things that I couldn't. I prayed, I really prayed." Jim poured out his heart, as if Jesus were hearing it for the first time. He spilled out his dashed hopes and dreams, his frustration with the resistance that came from the "control freaks" in the church, the agonizing days of preparing sermons that felt empty, and worst of all, the night voices that accused him and pummeled him with fear until sleep became impossible. "I just don't know how long I can take this," Jim sobbed. "I can't even pray anymore."

Jesus put his arm across Jim's shoulders and just sat with him. "I don't want you to have to take it any longer, Jim," He whispered.

Jesus told each one of them that He forgave them for holding grudges against Him and misunderstanding His intentions. In later conversations, when emotions weren't so raw, Jesus asked each of them to get a Bible and to do some study.

Jesus took each one of them to key places in the Scriptures. From passage to passage, He showed them that from the creation, God made people as His friends. He'd given them freedom of choice, unlike any other creature. God wanted partners to manage the earth, to rule it with the love and tenderness that He had formed within His "image bearers." Jesus also called their attention to the passages that described mankind's rebellion against God, and His heart-broken willingness to let us try to rule ourselves, to do things our way.

Passage after passage demonstrated how we traded the truth of God for a lie as we sinned against God and others. They saw how sin's consequences continually complicate real relationships with God and everyone else.

"Not one righteous," Jesus sighed. "The Father and I still loved you, but we had to let you experience the consequences of your rebellion. Now recall the story," Jesus said as He flipped through the pages of the Gospels, "of my coming to redeem you, to forgive you, and to give you a new start."

Barry and Lillian had heard the story a thousand times and Jim had preached about it Sunday after Sunday. But now, here with Jesus, it became personal and alive. They became characters in the long biblical line of human selfishness and God's corresponding patience.

Jesus explained, "But I didn't become man to make you slaves or robots or puppets; I came to heal you, to transform you, to give you abundant life in a new relationship of love with me. You're my child, my adult child. I'm calling you to cooperate with me. Let me walk you through ongoing transformation as we work together to bring my Kingdom to all. I want you to love *with* me, to lead *with* me, and to heal *with* me." Jesus' face revealed both sorrow for people's attempts to go it on their own and hope that it could be different.

One day, Barry stopped as he walked with Jesus in the field. He looked at the tender corn sprouts poking their shoots up in neat rows. Tearfully he turned to Jesus. "I'm so sorry, Lord, for the way I have expected You to be my slave, to make my plans work out the way I thought they should. But You wanted to help me grow up with your help, just like only You can make these sprouts grow."

Barry paused a long time as if something new slowly formed within him. He looked Jesus in the eyes and said, "Now I understand the feeling that came over me when I loved my wife and boys and wanted the very best for them. No wonder I feel such joy in planting seeds and watching them come up, imagining them full grown and beautiful, seeing them feed people in faraway places. That's the same joy You have, isn't it? I am so grateful to be Yours, Lord."

After their conversation in the office, Jesus and Jim walked into the Sanctuary of the church and sat in the front pew, staring at the cross for a long time. The morning sunlight filled the room with beauty and mystery. Jim turned to Jesus and tearfully confessed, "Love, freedom, sin, forgiveness, cooperation, Kingdom. They're all words I've studied and taught about, but why have I missed their meaning in my own heart? How could I have been so blind? I'm so sorry, Lord."

"My dear brother, these are relatively easy concepts for the head, but they bounce off a sin-hardened heart like pebbles off a boulder. I know you believe in me; you receive me as your Lord and Savior; you've served me for years; you even love me as much as you can. But hearts don't become soft overnight. I told my prophet Ezekiel once—you remember it—that I would give you a new heart and put a new spirit within you; and I would remove the heart of stone from your flesh and give you a heart of flesh. I would put My Spirit within you and cause you to walk in my statutes, and then you would be careful to observe My ordinances.

"But receiving a new heart takes time, Jim. And most of all, it takes your cooperation. I can't violate you by just doing things to you, by reprogramming your head and heart. You need to want to be like me, to seek my likeness, so we can accomplish this transformation together."

As Jim sat next to Jesus in the front of the church Sanctuary, he turned to Jesus and wept, "I'll take another hug if I may."

৪০৪০ ৫৩৫৩

Whether in the barn or field with Barry, the family room with Lillian, or the church with Jim, Jesus filled these times with healing and release. Each one felt stripped naked and then re-clothed with the most beautiful soft white linen robe. But Jesus offered more than this robe of righteousness, He offered them Presence and companionship. Yet, Jesus yearned to give them even more.

Chapter 5: Abundant Life

In another series of discussions, Jesus opened with, "There's another misunderstanding we need to talk about." He made that announcement first to Lillian after several early morning meetings in her family room. She found it interesting that the kids never woke up until after Jesus had left. Lillian would set her alarm for 5:15 A.M. so she could get up, get at least casually dressed, put on some makeup, and start the coffee. At precisely 5:30 A.M. Jesus would appear in the room. Sometimes He stood looking at a picture; other times sitting in a chair or staring out the window. He always greeted Lillian with a broad smile and a warm hug, like an old friend who had been anxiously awaiting the meeting. She also took note that He always complimented her on her coffee before He introduced the subject for the day. Many times Lillian had come with her own questions, but Jesus always took the lead. Interestingly, her questions were usually answered without her asking.

One morning, Jesus interrupted Lillian's first words, "Now hold on Lillian, I know you have questions, but we're not ready for that yet."

Jesus wanted to begin a new discussion and he started immediately.

"Lil (no one but her dad ever called her that), I'd like to ask you a question. What do you think about Abundant Life?" She felt awkward and uneasy. Here was the Person who invented the term asking her what she thought about it.

"Well, I suppose life is abundant when you have everything you need, maybe even more than you need."

"Good, go on. What do you need for your life to be really abundant?"

Lillian's face wrinkled and frowned as she looked down. Her life felt anything but abundant. Oh, she and Walt had saved enough money, owned a nice house and car, but when she compared their possessions to "abundance," she felt empty, harassed, lonely, and confused. Life hadn't turned out at all like she thought it would. In her mind, she reviewed her list of complaints: too much to do, frustration with the kids and with her own impatience, the lonely nights without Walt, her continued struggle with her weight, and finally, that damned church. She sheepishly looked up at Who sat patiently on the couch, waiting with warmth and understanding.

"Those issues are real, Lil. They frustrate you, they cause you fear, and sometimes they bring you a lot of pain." He paused and she recognized that Jesus understood her feelings, but didn't condemn her. Then He continued, "If I were to give you abundant life, would I have to make your kids act like mature adults, give you the wisdom of Solomon for your parenting, relocate Walter to a job here in town, and make sure he was home at the exact time each day and attentive to your every need? Maybe I could give you a tapeworm so you wouldn't gain weight." Jesus smiled. "How would you like me to remake your church; maybe bring Billy Graham as the pastor for a start?"

Lillian smiled but sat silently in her thoughts, although she wondered if her thoughts were ever silent to Him. She knew what He was getting at—the world isn't perfect; no one's life is perfect. Her eyes met His. "So what is abundant life?"

Jesus glanced at His watch, smiled, and put His hand on her shoulder, and then started for the door. "Think about it some, Lillian, and let's continue the conversation next time." He didn't bother to open the door as He passed through.

Jesus had similar discussions with Jim and Barry. Jim associated abundant life mostly with a church and ministry that worked. He wanted to bring people to Christ and help them to grow in their faith. He wanted the church to care for people in the community in a meaningful way. Most of all, he wanted the members to stop squabbling about everything.

Jesus interrupted Jim's thoughts as he prepared to make a second pass through his expectations. "Great aspirations, Jim. But I wonder. Would all that really make your life abundant? What if all those things happened and yet people didn't like you and rejected your ideas and leadership? Would the successful church you imagined be enough to make your life feel abundant?"

Jim pondered the question, first thinking that if the church became successful that might be good enough, but then realized how empty and lonely that felt. What did he really want?

Jesus waited for his line of thinking to play out and then said, "One way to get at it might be to ask yourself what keeps you up at night."

Jim mentally rehearsed a few recent sleepless nights. Financial insecurity seemed like a biggie. Yet what was it about the church finances—things weren't so bad that he'd lose his job or the lights would get turned off. No, it was what people thought of him, of his inability to cast a vision that motivated sacrificial giving—his failure as a leader.

He remembered Barry Anderson, the farmer with a bank account big enough to make a real difference, sitting in a congregational business meeting and almost jeering, "I'll not be the only one supporting this church, pastor. If you can't get other folks to step up, don't go looking to me." Then Barry folded his arms over his plump stomach, leaned back in his chair, and stared condemningly at Jim. Jim realized, of course, that more significant accusations lay behind Barry's statement than money. Barry had never recovered from his wife's prolonged cancer and death, and now he'd left the church altogether.

Jim recalled that day in the hospital room near the end when Barry had turned to him, red faced, and blurted out, "Well, why don't you do something? You're supposed to be the big man of prayer." Barry never even looked at Jim during the funeral and Jim felt like a failure at prayer as well.

Then Jim thought about the pew-sitters, like Lillian, who would nod off during his sermons. Even worse, she was elected to the Elder Board. He'd surmised that she thought that the financial problems would best be solved by getting a new pastor.

Jesus patiently waited, as Jim realized the terrible truth: Abundant life, for him, consisted in the approval of others. He wanted everyone to like him, to consider him successful and important, not only to love him but think him wonderful. He thought further about how defensive he could get when Kate would make suggestions about things at church, how angry he could feel when his son, Bryan, would act up on Sunday mornings, and how he hated to play golf with Phil, the Catholic priest who always beat him. Jim looked at Jesus in amazement, feeling hollow and ashamed.

"Old wounds," Jesus offered. "Your folks struggled to affirm you, always saying you could do better. That critical tendency dates back several generations actually, more on your father's side than your mother's. But both your parents learned early to try to help people become successful by criticizing them or telling them what they could have done better. Actually, Jim, you use the very same tactic on your family and your church." Jim nodded and shook his head.

Jesus went on in His frank and honest manner, "So, I suppose abundant life for you might be success on every front and the praise and accolades of everyone you know." Jesus raised an eyebrow with a slight grin. Jim knew Jesus was right and yet wasn't condemning him.

"How do I get that mess fixed?" Jim asked.

"Think about it for a while, my friend. We'll talk again later. Don't despair, there's hope." Another long hug and Jesus was gone.

ℰ℺℺ ℭℛℭℛ

"Abundant life?" Barry shouted. "There's no abundant life for me anymore. Any kind of life I had was stripped away when Elaine died. Watching her suffer tore my heart out. I know I own a successful farm and have money in the bank, but it doesn't mean squat without Elaine." Barry turned away from Jesus as he talked because he couldn't look at Him and still express the rage and despair he felt. "Hell, I would never have gotten anywhere without her. She was always so encouraging, so patient and wise in the face of my stubborn compulsiveness. She saved this farm a dozen times over. She raised our boys because I always worked. She did a damned good job, too," he snapped. Barry paused, slowly turning toward Jesus, and with a voice that sounded like a wounded animal, said angrily, "You want to give me abundant life? You give me Elaine back!"

Jesus looked at Barry's red face and swollen eyes. Tears streamed down Jesus' cheeks. "I'm so sorry for your pain, Barry. I am so sorry that you lost Elaine. Death is a terrible thing and cancer can be a terrible way to die. I stood with you at her bedside when you told me you'd do anything to save her. I was with you in the barn when you threw that brick through the window. I shared every ounce of your pain, Barry. I am so sorry you lost Elaine."

Barry softened and with pleading eyes leaned toward Jesus, "Then why didn't You do something?"

"I didn't take the cancer away, but I did a lot, Barry. I gave Elaine real peace and strength during the ordeal. You saw it. I gave you strength time after time. Two people came to believe in me because I helped Elaine share her faith. There's much more."

"But why didn't You save her? You have the power," Barry said accusingly.

Jesus and Barry stood quietly for a time, and then Jesus sat down on a bale of hay directly across from Barry and looked him in the eyes. "I did save her, Barry. Elaine was born with a genetic defect that made her vulnerable to the Radon in the soil and the nuclear pollution from the bomb testing. Her immune system also weakened because she worried so much. Fear wreaks havoc in our bodies, Barry. There are millions of people like Elaine who suffer at the hands of the world's corruption every day. It breaks Our heart. The Father and I discussed whether or not to intervene in Elaine's disease, but for reasons I cannot possibly explain, We chose to let her come home sooner rather than later. I know it broke your heart, Barry, but it was the right thing for Us to do."

After a long pause, Jesus continued, "She's safe with the Father and me, Barry. She has her reward now, enjoying love and beauty beyond her imagination. Her parents feel so overjoyed to have her with them again. She's becoming the beautiful being that you only saw glimpses of. She is truly happy, Barry, because she feels your love and completely trusts you and your boys to me. Would you want Me to tear her away from all that?"

Barry just stared off across the barn. Jesus stood, stepped to Barry, and embraced him with a strength that felt like soft steel. He held him so close that each could feel the other's heartbeat, as Jesus' face pressed against the stalwart farmer's tear stained cheek.

Jesus whispered into Barry's ear, "My dear friend, I came to give you abundant life. Elaine wants it for you; I want it for you. Take some time alone and think about what real abundant life might be like for you, until you join Elaine in heaven. We'll talk about it again soon." Jesus tenderly withdrew, headed toward the barn door, and vanished into the morning light.

The next individual meetings with Jim, Lillian, and Barry followed the same pattern Jesus had used in the previous conversations about sin and forgiveness. At just the right time He stated, "Get your Bible and let's do some study." Jesus and Barry always met in the barn, so Barry had to go into the house to fetch his. Jesus met Jim in his office, so Jim grabbed for the shelf.

"What translation?" he quipped with a smirk.

Jesus and Lillian met in her family room, as usual, so her worn and marked Bible lay handy.

Jesus started them off with the famous passage in John, chapter 10, verse 10: "I came that they may have life, and have it abundantly." This time, instead of just laying it out, He helped them dig into the meaning with some questions.

"What's the context?" he asked. All three answered that Jesus made the statement as He described Himself as the Good Shepherd. "Good, replied Jesus. "Go on."

Lillian offered, "You're my Good Shepherd, so as one of Your sheep, I should have abundant life, right?"

"Well," Jesus responded, "the text really says that I came to give you 'life.' Life would be in contrast to...? That's right, death. I made another comparison in that conversation."

The answer came quickest to Jim. It was one of his favorite passages. "You contrasted Yourself with the thief who comes to steal, kill, and destroy."

"You got it, Jim. Who's the thief?"

Barry was quick on the draw with that one. "Hell, it's the devil."

Lillian had more trouble. "I don't know, maybe the thief represented the Pharisees or just some sheep robber."

Jesus pushed her a little further. "Lillian, who does the Bible say always tries to steal your happiness, kill all your hopes, and destroy your life forever? Do you know anyone around here trying to do that to you?"

Lillian thought for a few minutes. "No, no there isn't. I suppose the Bible would call it the devil, but isn't all that just figurative? Doesn't the 'devil' represent all the evil in the world?"

Jesus responded with a smile, "Lil, you have to believe what you read in My Book. Can you imagine that all the evil deeds and intentions in the world, and throughout history, could get together with one purpose and intention, cooperating with one another, until they could be called the Prince of this World?"

"No, I suppose that does seem farfetched."

Jesus continued, "Once a beautiful angel, named Lucifer, rebelled against God. He chose to rule in darkness if he could not rule in heaven. He deceived many other angels, all cast out of heaven into this world. He thinks he owns it. He thinks you belong to him, or at least that you'll become his. He wants to steal, kill, and destroy your very life, just to get back at God who loves you. He's been messing with your mind a lot lately."

Lillian just looked at Jesus silently, reflecting on the "unfortunate circumstances" that, in fact, were squeezing the life out of her.

Somewhere in their barn conversation, Barry blurted out, "You mean that the devil killed Elaine?"

"No, Barry. He doesn't have the power to do that. Life and death lie within my control now. But, what do you think the devil's been trying to kill in you and in your boys?"

Barry scratched his chin, then his eyes widened, "My hope, my joy, and my faith. I haven't talked with the boys about it, but maybe that's why they've stopped coming to church too."

"Right on all accounts."

Jim was the first to make the next connection in response to Jesus' question, "So, what is life abundantly? What does it mean in the context of the conversation I had with my first disciples?"

Jim responded immediately, "Life, eternal life, comes through being Your sheep, by belonging to You. You provide everything I need or could ever want, as long as my needs and wants are focused on life in your Kingdom, your flock."

"Exactly. In faith you've received my gift of forgiveness and eternal life. I adopted you into my Kingdom as my child. All that I have is now yours."

Jim understood his place as God's adopted child, but it seemed as though its reality only sank in as Jesus spoke. "All?" Jim pondered in his mind. "What does that mean?" Jim found the implications staggering. "How much more abundant could life get than that?"

ഇഇ ങങ

The next question became the show-stopper in each of the three discussions. Jesus asked, "So if I give you eternal life and promise to shepherd you and supply all your needs, what don't you have, that you still want?" All three of Jesus' friends became silent. They each mentally recalled the litany that they'd spread before Jesus, the list of things wrong with their lives. "Good," said Jesus. "With that picture, you're ready for the next part of the lesson. From your list of distresses, identify what you're afraid will be stolen and destroyed. Let's get to the bottom of this."

Each one responded in light of their previous conversations with Jesus. Jim shared that he was afraid that the worth of his life would be lost; that he would look back, see only failure, and discover that his life had no meaning. Finally, he added to the list, "Most of all, I'm afraid that I won't be loved."

Lillian responded to Jesus' question, "Lord, I feel like I'm losing my peace and safety; maybe it's already being stolen. Family is the most important thing to me, and I'm afraid that I'll fail my kids; that they'll go astray as they grow up. I'm afraid that Walt will love his work more than me and I'll lose him. I'm afraid that all the stress at church will kill my faith."

Jesus responded tenderly, "And what if all that did happen to you, Lil?"

After a few minutes Lillian turned to Jesus, and sobbed, "I think I would die."

"Ahh," replied Jesus, "Now we've come to the bottom of fear."

Barry sat on a hay bale and looked Jesus in the eyes. "I'm afraid that the love and laughter I once knew will be taken from me. I'm afraid, without Elaine around, that the boys will realize what a jerk I really am and that I'll lose them and their love. I'm afraid I will die an angry old man who curses God and loses everything."

Jesus told each one of them to spend some time in His Book and let the Holy Spirit guide their reading. They would meet again the next day at the same time and place.

All three found themselves bewildered. Never before had they faced their fears this openly. Never before had they realized that the blackness of death lay at the bottom of everything they feared. It was frightening to see the power that the "thief" exercised in each of their lives. "How could this happen to a Christian?" Jim sobbed, as if speaking for them all.

But that evening, after they completed their various chores and had time alone, each one picked up the Bible, "His Book." Neither Barry nor Lillian knew where to look for what Jesus wanted them to see. Jim had always been skeptical of the "close your eyes, open your Bible, and point" tactic. So all three sat in silence, interestingly all at about the same time in the evening, and waited.

They thought about their first meetings with Jesus in the flesh, about their fright and skepticism. They recalled Jesus' ordinary appearance and manner—no halos, bright shining lights, or miracles—just love, profound love, and His persistence in pursuing their hearts. "Where's all this going?" they each asked themselves, almost in unison.

Jim felt drawn to return to the John 10 passage that Jesus used to begin this discussion. He read verse 11. "I am the good shepherd; the good shepherd lays down His life for the sheep." Then, without really thinking about it, he turned to Psalm 23. "The Lord is my shepherd, I shall not want." He read through the Psalm slowly and sat in silence as he let each word and thought sink into his soul. Finally his fingers found the most quoted verse in the Bible, John 3:16: "For God so loved the world (his mind heard, "You, Jim.") that He gave His only begotten son, that whoever believes in Him shall not perish, but have eternal (Jim read, "Abundant") life."

Jim mused, "I've believed in Jesus for heaven, but have I believed in Him for life here and now, for abundant life? Have I looked to Him for the love my soul seeks and the safety from death that I so fear? No, I've looked to the favor of others and the success of my church and ministry. That's gotta change."

Lillian did the "close your eyes, open the Bible, and point" thing. She opened to John 15, verses 9 to 11. "Just as the Father has loved Me, I have also loved you; abide in my love. If you keep my commandments, you will abide in my love; just as I have kept my Father's commandments and abide in His love. These things I have spoken to you so that my joy may be in you, and that your joy may be made full." Before she knew what she was doing, her left-hand finger held her place in John while her right-hand flipped right. Something, Someone in her, told her to look at the end of the story. Her fingers opened to Revelation

61

21, verses 3 and 4, where John describes the new heaven and the new earth. As she read, these verses captivated her heart: "He will dwell among them, and they shall be His people, and God Himself will be among them, and He will wipe away every tear from their eyes; and there will no longer be any death; there will no longer be any mourning, or crying, or pain...."

"Yeah, but that's in heaven," Lillian reflected. Then the light came on. "Oh my goodness. Yes that's all complete in heaven, but Jesus lives here now, too, whether I can see Him or not. He IS dwelling among us. Death isn't the last word for His children, nor are the things that make us afraid all powerful. The joy and peace I've always longed for can't come from this world, its stuff, or its people. I've been looking in the wrong places!"

Barry had a harder time. First he looked up "abundant life" in his concordance. That took him back to the John 10 passage. Then he looked up "fear." He'd have to read nearly the whole Bible to get through all that. Then he looked up "death," which only made him more exasperated. Finally, a thought came to him: "Look in Elaine's Bible."

Barry went to the nightstand where he kept Elaine's worn and marked up Bible. A deep longing for Elaine rose up within him as he remembered the long hours she'd spent with her Bible. Ribbons marked several pages and the red one caught Barry's eye. He opened it to Jeremiah 29, and started with verse 11. The passage had been underlined and marked with highlighter. He read, "For I know the plans that I have for you,' declares the LORD, 'plans for welfare and not for calamity, to give you a future and a hope. Then you will call upon me and come and pray to me, and I will listen to you. You will seek me and find me. When you search for me with all your heart, I will be found by you,' declares the Lord."

Barry reflected, "A future and a hope... when I seek God with all my heart. I don't think I've ever done that, not really. I've believed all the right things, tried to act nice to people and help out the needy and attended church almost all my life. I've asked for lots of things but never really sought Him, personally. It's always been about me, not about loving God."

Then Barry noticed the yellow ribbon. Another passage had been marked with a big asterisk beside it. The verse John 14:6 read, "Jesus said to him, "I am the way, and the truth, and the life; no one comes to the Father but through Me."

Barry dropped to his knees at the side of the bed. "Jesus, I know you can hear me, even if I can't see you. I want you to know that I realize what abundant life is—it is You! My God, it's You."

Jesus met with each one the next day at their appointed times. "What did you learn?" Jesus asked.

Each shared the Scripture passages they'd found and what the passage had meant to them. Each one, uniquely echoed the words of Barry: "You, Lord, are abundant life. When I am Yours, with You, I have nothing to fear."

Jesus put His arms around each one and whispered, "I didn't come to just give you good *things;* I came to give you me, my Father, and the Holy Spirit. In Us, you have real life. You're safe from the power of sin, the devil, and this world." As He turned to leave He said to each one, "The trouble is, you have to learn to live in abundant life. It doesn't come naturally for my fallen people. Let's meet again next week—same time, same place."

The following conversations with Jim, Lillian, and Barry became more casual, walks in the park or field. Jesus even told Jim that He wanted to play golf with him. Jim looked up with disbelief and retorted, "It's hard to imagine You'd want to play golf in the first place, but the thought of me playing against God seems pretty futile. I lose often enough, as it is."

Jesus grinned. "Let's just go and have some fun."

In these casual times each one began to process what they'd learned about abundant life. They reflected about how they had grown up to depend on everything but Jesus, expressing regret that they had been so selfish and expected God to jump to their commands.

Jim put it this way, "I've always known the greatest commandment, that I should love You with my whole heart, mind, soul, and strength. But I guess I never really thought it was possible. I assumed that serving You as a pastor would be enough love, I guess."

Jesus responded to each of their confessions, "It's sort of like growing up, isn't it? We start out as babies, needing and demanding. We become adolescents and begin to figure out how we can make the world work for us, to meet our own needs. Finally, if we truly become spiritually mature adults, we learn that the world and God are bigger than we can ever manage to control. So, we learn to adapt, to care about the needs of others. You learn to take yourself out of center place and let God be God, our God. As He reveals Himself to you, you come to love Him and live in His love. As you continue to grow up, that relationship of love becomes your ground, your hope, your life. It's a lifelong process and I'm inviting you to live as my brother, my sister, an adult child of the Heavenly Father." Jim realized that Jesus understood this process personally from His own experience as He grew from a baby in Bethlehem to a boy in Nazareth and finally into a man.

Each nodded, wanting to live as God's children, but they also felt bewildered.

Jim expressed his bewilderment as he sighed after hitting another golf ball into the rough, "Abundant life with You seems so attractive, but I'm doing it the only way I know how, and it's not working."

Lillian, in her conversation with Jesus, responded, "That sounds wonderful, but how do I develop that way with everything that's going on in my life?"

Barry, true to his character, put it bluntly, "Well, Lord, maybe there are some of us who are just too stupid."

The next week, Jesus met with each of them, Jim in his office, Lillian in her family room, and Barry in his barn. Jesus started the conversation as soon as they'd shared greetings and hugs, "You're beginning to understand the first part of my calling to you, to let me love and forgive you and for you to learn to live in the abundance of my love. As I told you before, learning to live in abundant life takes a lifetime of letting go of the things in this world, things and people that tempt you to rely on them for love, safety, success, and power. You have to learn to trust my love and to depend on me for every need. When I become your rock and your basic needs are met in me, then you're free to enjoy the love and friendship of others without needing something from them. You'll be able to accept yourself as less than perfect and forgive yourself as I forgive you. With my strength, you'll be able to face the trials of life without fearing that they will destroy you. Just be patient with yourself. I am!" Jesus grinned at each one and finished, "It's simple!"

Chapter 6: Presence Beyond

The amazing events of the past few weeks have gone unnoticed by the rest of the Emmaus population. However, significant changes have already begun in a circle wider than the three people visited by Jesus. No, Jim, Lillian, and Barry haven't said a word to anyone about meeting with Jesus, as hard as that's been. But subtle seeds of change that will affect the whole town have begun to sprout, first deep within the hearts of three simple followers of Jesus, and then among those they touch. Presence has radiated beyond.

Through the series of personal visits, a new and radically vibrant relationship with Jesus emerged within Jim, Lillian, and Barry. While they'd believed in Him for years, and even known Him to some extent, the relationship definitely changed. For them, Jesus had once been almost like a mythical figure, somewhere in another dimension. Yes, they knew that their prayers were able to break through that other dimension, but they had never experienced Him as personally present in the way He had really been, all along. While they wouldn't dare say they now knew the whole of Jesus, some of the significant barriers to knowing Him have been removed. For each one, issues of sin, forgiveness, love, and misunderstanding needed to be dealt with before the relationship could truly become an open and safe place.

As they learned to know Jesus, present, each one came to like Him as a person and loved Him as their Lord. Not many people think about actually "liking" Jesus. You can only like someone when you come to know their personality, see how they act and live. It's hard to do that with "the man upstairs," on the other end of an endless list of requests. Our three all lived busy and full lives, but now everything in everyday revolved around Jesus and what they were learning and discovering. Other than when to meet and maybe what Bible passage they were to review, Jesus had given no instructions to change. Yet many things had begun to change.

For example, Jim, particularly, began to find prayer confusing. For a time, he made lists of things to talk to Jesus about the next time they met.

One day, Jesus responded to one of those lists, "You know that I am still just as close to you whether or not you can see or hear me; just say what you want to say or think what you think and I'll know it. Be still for a bit afterwards, and you might be surprised by my response. Remember, I'm with you always." Jesus' broad smile assured Jim he wasn't being scolded.

Lillian, like Jim and Barry, also struggled in new ways with Bible study. At first, they'd listen for special words or a Bible passage they were supposed to turn to, as they would when He was physically present. But soon, they realized that, as they waited, thoughts came with a certain feel to them, the same feeling that came when He was actually talking out loud. They learned to recognize His voice even though they didn't "hear" anything. In each of them, the fear and anxiety that had been so ever-present were gradually replaced by faith, hope, and trust. Without that dampening weight of fear, they began to act more like themselves, with more energy to relate to others.

Keeping the secret proved hard, however. Kate immediately began asking Jim what was going on. "Jim, you seem so distracted, like your mind has been somewhere else. Is something wrong? You know you can talk about it. Are you afraid of something going wrong at church?"

Jim thought silently, "I've always been open with Kate and I hate it that she feels like I'm hiding something." After a few days, he realized that he had to open up to Kate, to give her some kind of reassurance. One evening after dinner, Jim said, "Honey, I know I owe you an explanation for how I've been acting lately. There's nothing wrong; in fact some really good things are happening, they're happening inside me. I've been spending more time in prayer, really talking to Jesus, and trying to listen to Him, as well. The listening part has blessed me the most. I've realized that I've been carrying the weight of this church way too much, that I'd better let the Lord carry it before I burn out. In these prayer times, I'm discovering some difficult things about myself and some amazing things about the Lord."

Jim went on to share with Kate how he'd been trying to meet his own needs for affirmation through church success. "I know I've been placing a lot of those same needs on you too, Kate. I'm really sorry. I guess I've grown up with a pretty low self-image, thinking that I have to prove to myself that I am worthwhile through winning the approval of others. I know now that my identity and self-worth must be based on the Lord's love and acceptance. It's the only way I can love you just for who you are and be free to fully accept your love with no strings attached on my end."

Kate teared up and threw her arms around him, "Oh, Honey, I love you so very much. Sometimes I do feel as if I can't fully meet your needs and I want to so badly."

Jim kissed her on the cheek and held her in a long embrace. "Just being you is all I need, Kate."

Jim became more attentive to Kate as well as their son, Brian. A "special needs child," Brian had been a handful ever since he was born. Attention deficit along with severe mood swings made him a challenge, especially in church. Kate hadn't been able to work outside the home because parenting Brian proved a full-time job. Brian's diagnosis and prognosis were unclear. The doctors and specialists told Jim and Kate that it would take a lot longer than three years to see how the disorder would progress. But they warned that it would get worse.

Jim was praying for Brian and for his own patience one night, when he pictured Brian playing with a dog. The more he thought about it, the more he wondered if the Lord might be speaking. He talked to Kate and they decided to look into the possibility of buying a puppy for Brian. The specialists, however, said that a trained companion dog might prove more helpful. Jim and Kate planned to pursue the possibility, although they worried that these highly trained dogs would be too expensive. They agreed to pray about it and Kate asked her Bible study group to pray with them.

ഓഓ ങങ

Living only a few blocks away, Lillian also experienced some significant changes. She found that her early mornings with Jesus had become precious, whether or not she could see Him. Most mornings she was up at 5:30 AM. Beginning her prayer time with a Bible verse, she would spend most of the hour sitting silently with a listening heart, as she did when Jesus was physically there. She never heard the same direct and confronting words, like she did when Jesus actually appeared, but the same sense of safety, love, and presence would often come over her. In His "presence," Lillian would let the agenda of her day pass through her mind, trusting each piece to her Lord. She began to realize that she didn't have to tell God how to run the universe. She could simply hold her concerns before Him, verbally or silently, and trust Him as her Good Shepherd.

When Walt came home that weekend, she fixed him a special dinner after the kids were fed and in bed. She explained that she'd been praying more lately and realized how hard she'd been to live with. "When you return home on Fridays, I complain about the week and then dump as much of the house responsibility on you as I can." She confessed how selfish she had been in not attending to how tired he was, as well. "I think the Lord is asking me to find a better way of handling my end of our parenting and to save more of me for you," she said tenderly. "Would you help me figure out how to do that?"

Walt and Lillian agreed to pray together on the phone each day that he was away, asking God to guide them in their responsibilities and help them love others more in each of their encounters. They began to feel a new intimacy in knowing what the other faced that day, sharing it together, and remembering to pray for one another throughout the day.

Lillian had always dreaded the first Wednesday evening of each month, when the church Elder Board met at Emmaus Church. Usually full of tension, the meetings had always seemed to focus on whatever appeared wrong in the church. With the church finances stretched, there was always plenty wrong. Although the Elder meetings had been downright depressing for everyone, something was changing; the last two meetings seemed particularly different.

For one thing, Pastor Jim seemed different. Usually wired tight and eager to get through the agenda, he started leading an extended devotion to open the meeting. Unlike the usual quick Bible verse and hurried prayer, he introduced a thought that had come to him that week, and asked people to think of a Bible verse that might speak to it. He then had the group spend at least five minutes in silent prayer. After the prayer time he asked for personal reflections. Both because the "listening to Jesus" time represented something new and because most of the Board members were as anxious to get done with the meeting as Lillian had been, some felt a bit restless. One man even challenged the pastor, wondering if they really had enough time for this addition to their "business meeting."

Lillian flabbergasted herself when she spoke up and defended Pastor Jim, "Maybe if we listen to God more, He might just guide us through the problems we're facing." She went home from the last Elder meeting actually inspired. Jesus seemed present.

Barry's transitions progressed pretty uncomfortably at first. He felt like an elk shedding his rack without intending to. He'd been crusty enough all his life, but after Elaine died he'd put the antlers way out there to keep people at a distance, not wanting anyone to see his pain or anger at God. Everyone close to Barry could see what was happening, of course. But as he became "friends" with Jesus, the hard exterior began to melt away. Margaret, his housekeeper, almost fell over when he noticed the freshly waxed kitchen floors.

"Margaret, that floor looks absolutely beautiful. Why, it makes the whole room shine with light; makes it a happier place."

"Why thank you, Mr. Barry!" she exclaimed.

One day, Barry called his boys, Aaron and Ben, and asked if he could come over some morning and ride tractor with each of them. Almost to the word, they responded, "Sure, Dad. What's the problem?"

"No problem, I'm just missing you and thought we'd chew the fat."

Aaron and Benjamin, two years apart, have always been the pride of their father's heart. But since their mom died, Barry had grown distant. Now he wanted to change that.

On each ride he asked Aaron and then Ben how they were doing with their mother's death. After the family custom of answering, "Fine," had been honored, each one shared how much they missed their mom and struggled with why God let her die so young. Maybe for the first time in years, Barry didn't interrupt with advice, but sat and listened and nodded as they shared. After some silence, as the tractor turned for another swath, Barry apologized for not being there for the boys. "I was so damned selfish; all I could see or feel was my own hurt and anger," he confessed.

Ben looked surprised. "Anger, Dad? Who were you angry at?"

"I was angry at God, son. I felt that He had treated me and you boys unjustly by letting that cancer take your mom." Another long pause and Barry went on, "But we got all that straightened out, Jesus and me. He forgave me and I forgave Him. She's happy with Him in heaven now, and we'll do just fine here, with God's help."

Aaron sat and listened to his dad's request for forgiveness. Barry also asked Aaron to forgive him for always pushing him to do better. "I was always so proud of you, son, but I was afraid to show it or tell you. I so wanted you to do well and I thought I needed to keep the pressure on, the way my dad did. In my prayers, lately, I've realized how the Lord does just the opposite with me. He loves me and encourages me, even when I mess up. Your mother was the same way. I was just too blind to see that I was doing it all backwards. I'd really like to be your friend, son."

Aaron leaned over and touched his father's cheek. "I love you, Dad. I have been angry with you sometimes about being treated the harshest. But I do forgive you. Let's work at that friend thing. I'd like that a lot."

"The Lord will help us if we ask Him," Barry responded.

The next Sunday, Barry showed up for church and sat in his traditional spot in the pew. He was startled to see "his" Anderson families in church. He thought they'd stopped going, so didn't say anything about it, so as not to embarrass them. For some reason, going back to church seemed like the hardest step of obedience he had to take. While he felt reconciled to Jesus, the church was another matter. He'd never really liked church, even though he'd served as an elder. There just seemed to be something missing. Not only were things disorganized, but now he realized that it had all felt empty, like a store without merchandise, or a play without actors, or..., he said to himself, "like religion without Jesus." People received him politely, but Barry didn't really want to be there. However, he had to follow through with forgiveness, and the church had been the recipient of some pretty harsh judgments on his part. On the way out, after avoiding shaking hands with the pastor, Barry thought to himself, "I may have to forgive this church, but it doesn't change the fact that it's more of a religious club than anything."

A couple of weeks later Barry had dinner with Ben and Aaron and their families. Eventually church came up in the conversation and Aaron's wife commented about how good Pastor Jim's sermons had been lately. "Instead of just being fed information," she reflected, "I feel like I'm being introduced to a person, to Jesus. I really like the way the pastor talks about Him." She went on, "I was in a prayer group with his wife, Kate, last week. Several of my friends invited me to go. She asked for prayer about getting their son, Brian, a dog, one of those companion dogs, I think they call them. The doctors believe it might make Brian more peaceful and happy. But companion dogs really cost a lot of money with all the training they get."

"What does a dog like that cost," Barry asked.

"I think it is something like five thousand dollars," Aaron chimed in. "A charity pays the other half."

The next day, Barry sold some of his best cattle. He cashed the check and put exactly five thousand dollars in a sealed envelope and included a note. "A dog can be a man (or boy's) best friend." Of course the note and envelope were unsigned. Pastor Jim found it the next Sunday on the pulpit, with another inscription written on the envelope, "Open AFTER church."

℘℘ ℘℘

The Emmaus Church congregation also began to reflect the "visitations" without realizing it. Pastor Jim seemed so much happier and his sermons more personal, humble, and relatable. Worship attendance increased, too. Of course Aaron and Ben and their families filled two pews. While only Lillian had usually attended, Walt and the kids were frequently with her now. Barry's scowl had given way to a welcoming smile, and the surprise and delight about it seemed infectious in the whole congregation.

The church service continued pretty much the same, although it seemed that the prayers lasted a bit longer and had spaces in them. Pastor Jim would often say, "Let's just be still with the Lord for a minute." Members left services each Sunday feeling different, feeling better. No one could quite put a finger on any one thing, but it felt good. Strangely, giving increased some as well.

One day, out of the blue, Jim decided to ask Father Phil to play golf.

"You're doing what?" Kate challenged, "You hate to play golf with Phil; he always kills you."

"I know. It just came to mind as something I ought to do."

Surprised, but delighted, the Catholic Priest accepted the invitation. They met early the next morning at the clubhouse. "It's early enough not to slow others down; let's just play through, just the two of us," Jim suggested.

"I'd like that," Father Phil responded. It wasn't long before Father Phil quipped, "Been taking lessons, Jim? Your swing has improved a lot; in fact, I would say it's darn good."

"No lessons. Just watching a friend of mine play."

As they walked on to the next hole, Jim reflected on Phil's comment about his improved swing. "Strange," he thought. Books and lessons hadn't improved his game. But as he watched Jesus play golf, his own body just seemed to learn, wanting to imitate Him. He wondered if that was why Jesus' disciples spent so much time with Him. "Is it being with Jesus that changes us more than what we learn?" he wondered.

Better swing or not, Phil beat Jim by four strokes. After the game, they sat in the "Cooler Shack" at the City Golf Course and drank a soda. All the "wind-and-weather" niceties exhausted in the nine holes, meaningful conversation now seemed appropriate. Jim opened with an honesty surprising among clergy. "You know, Phil, it's been really hard this year at Emmaus Community. Attendance and giving have been down and there's been so much bickering. I've taken it way too personally, beating myself up pretty badly, feeling like a failure. I wish I knew how to cooperate with Jesus better."

Phil sat silently for a bit and then responded and shared his own story. "I can understand how you feel, Jim. I haven't been feeling so hot about myself lately, either. Things at St. Timothy's seem always the same—boring. The same people come and go, but their eyes seem glazed over. It's as if Jesus wasn't anywhere around, not in the Mass or in my homily. I've been counting the years until the Bishop decides to transfer me out of this dead-end town. But, 'you-know-what' may well freeze over before that happens."

The two pastors went on to discuss the town, the little town where nothing much happens, where no one expects anything to happen, and people like it that way. Jim interjected, "I had dreams about building a growing successful church. Maybe that feels out of place to people here. But I've also realized that I've been trying to grow the church for the wrong reasons."

"What do you mean?" Phil asked.

Phil looked Jim in the eyes as Jim continued, "It's been all about me and my hopes and dreams; it was never about the people in this town and Jesus' love for them. I've been experiencing some real renewal in my faith lately, so I am not as discouraged. But that doesn't mean I know how to pastor that church any differently."

Phil responded, "It's really encouraging to hear that I'm not the only one who's confused. Maybe what people in this town need is a visit from Jesus, like what happened with its namesake—Emmaus."

Jim grew quiet and thoughtful. "Jesus has visited this town; He's visited me," he mused silently. "Now what am I going to do about it? I can't tell anyone."

Phil interrupted Jim's thought, "You know, I'll bet that we're not the only clergy in this area who feel this way. Today has been like a breath of fresh air for me. I mean, who can you talk to about this stuff? What if we invite the other pastors in town and some of the country pastors to coffee and get to know one another better? If a Catholic and a Protestant asked together, maybe they would come." Jim said immediately, 'That sounds like a great idea," and then paused. "Let's agree to pray about it first, though, check it with the Lord, and see if we're as excited about it next week, maybe after another golf game?"

"You're on, Reverend Cline," Father Phil laughed.

Neither of them could possibly know what was born in the Cooler Shack that hot summer day. Emmaus' first Ministerial Association began a year later. Gradually, the pastors learned to know and trust one another. Their mutual encouragement brought new hope and energy to the faith leaders. Their new-found trust and mutual support gradually spread to the churches in the community. People were actually encouraged to visit other churches and bring back what they found meaningful.

The Ministerial Association eventually coordinated the work of the town's churches to help the poor. The rural poor can get lost more easily than those who live in city slums. In towns like Emmaus, the poor live on farms, in trailer houses, basements, and spare rooms spread all over the county. Working with local agencies, people who needed help were located, interviewed and often helped to get on their feet. A sense of pride began to emerge in Emmaus, not because "nothing ever changed," but because of the sense of caring that emerged. Jesus had been present in the town of Emmaus ever since its founding. But now, because a few took His presence seriously, His presence began to make a real difference. Changes like that have a domino effect that goes far beyond the confines of any small town.

Chapter 7: Discipleship

"I think You're asking the impossible," Jim half shouted and half groaned, with his arms folded on his chest. The conversation had actually begun earlier when Jesus introduced his next topic for discussion.

Jesus continued, "We've been talking about the abundant life that I want for my sons and daughters. I'm really pleased by the way you've gotten to the core of what gets in the way of this wonderful life that can be yours. Your new desire to more fully receive my love and to trust me to provide for your needs has helped you release your dependence on the counterfeits that the world touts. You see, Jim, I've established two levels of calling on your life. My "first order call" invites you to live as my beloved; that's the foundation for abundant life. But there's more, much more. My "second order call" invites you to follow me."

Jesus persisted in the more arduous process of taking Jim the next step into the abundance of discipleship.

"We're talking about my second order call to you, Jim. It's not impossible at all. I will teach you how to follow me." Jesus paused to let Jim regain his footing. Finding assent in Jim's nod, Jesus went on, "Let me give you some background. You've heard it before, but let me remind you." Jesus resettled Himself in the chair and continued. "Before the beginning of time, I looked into the future and saw you and loved you – not just people in general, Jim, but you specifically. I longed for you to work with me in redeeming the world and establishing my

Kingdom here on earth; I wanted you to be my partner, my coworker, my companion in my Father's plan of mercy. But for that to happen, here and now, you have to learn to follow me."

Jim was quick to respond, "Lord, that's what I want, too. I thought that's what I've been doing."

Jesus looked into Jim's eyes and spoke the truth, "Jim, part of you wants that, but as you've learned, the other part of you wants acceptance, approval, and success to prove that you're a worthwhile person. You determined to gain those things through the noblest cause you could think of, my Church. But your motives weren't the only thing that had been deformed by the world; your method got tweaked as well. You depended on principles of church leadership rather than following me. Using your own wisdom to try to build my Kingdom, you asked me to bless and empower the strategy that seemed right to you. When things went well, you basked in the accolades of others rather than in my love; when things went wrong, you blamed me. You asked me to follow you rather than help you follow me. When you did try to follow me, you did it as though I wasn't really here. We need to turn all that around."

Jim sat silently for a long time. Finally, he responded in a tone that seemed to emanate from the floor beneath him, "I guess You're right. But I don't know how to turn that around, to follow You. It is one thing to have you sitting in my office, but it's another when I can't see or hear you. I still think You're asking the impossible."

৪৩৪৩ ৪৩৪৩

Barry's and Lillian's conversations followed pretty much the same lines. Jesus shared about His first order call to live in mutual abundant love, and His second order invitation, to follow Him in bringing His love and healing to the world. Both responded at first by trying to get themselves off the hook.

Barry explained, "I am only a farmer, Jesus; what do I know about bringing Your Kingdom on earth? Are you saying

You want me to become a minister or something? Hell, I don't even like church."

Lillian reacted, "But Jesus, You know that I have kids to raise and a husband to take care of and a household to run. I donate time to church, but there isn't anything left of me to do more."

Jesus, sitting on the edge of His chair (or hay bale, in Barry's case), looked intently at each one as He said, "It's not that you have to do something 'more;' you're right where I want you. I have positioned you perfectly to partner with me. There isn't anything more you have to do except follow me in the *way you* do what you're already doing."

"Barry, We have called you to be Our touch of love to your family, friends, and church. Lots of people out there hate church. But it's not me they don't like; they just don't see me in the folks who go there. People need to experience me IN YOU, Barry. They're struggling; you can see that."

Barry looked down, deep in thought, and then looked Jesus in the eyes. "I'm trying. You've seen how I've tried to reach out more, to love more. What more do You want me to do?"

Jesus smiled. "Barry, you try to figure out what to do yourself. Ask me what to do, and then follow me in the way I guide you. It would be like hiring a farmhand who had never plowed before and just pointing him to the tractor. He might have wonderful intentions, but the tractor and the field would suffer. I've told you in my Book, that I go before you. I've designed the Kingdom in such a way that it takes both of us working together. You're my partner, Barry, but can I see and know what you can't."

Barry almost sputtered, "That sounds easy enough when I can actually see You and hear Your voice, but what about the rest of the time?" Then Barry became more honest. "Besides, I'm afraid that You'll ask me to do something that I don't want to do or can't do."

Jesus smiled and put His hand on Barry's arm. "I understand, Barry. There were times when I felt the same way about my mission from the Father. But trust me; I'll never ask you to do something that we can't do together. It may take courage and perseverance, but I will always give you the necessary wisdom and power. When you try to play it safe, you miss the wonders of abundant life. But as you follow me and partner with me in this grand adventure, when you lose your life for me, abundant life will spring up in you and all around you."

Barry sighed. "Even if I weren't so selfish, I don't know how to follow you, Lord."

"I'll show you how, Barry. That's why I'm here."

ജ ജ ര ര

In response to Lillian's push-backs, Jesus explained that she'd been called to do everything she's currently doing, not on her own, but with His leadership, strength, wisdom, and power. "I'm a pretty good parent, you know," he quipped to Lillian with a smile. "Lillian, your life can become amazingly exciting when you and I work together. Every encounter you have becomes an opportunity for us to bless, love, and encourage. You don't necessarily have to present the Gospel or even bring up God. You just enter into the relationship as you listen to your heart and to me. With the inner wisdom of the Holy Spirit, you'll know how to be present to others with a word, or just a kind smile. If people's hearts hunger for me or seek me, even in the slightest, they'll receive my touch in a profound way through you. That person may never know what's happened, but a seed will have been planted. In the same way, your kindness may water a seed that I planted through someone else. You'll be surprised to see what happens, not because you worked at it, but because you were attentive and responsive to my Presence. In time, following me becomes the most natural thing, and people around you will be blessed beyond your imagination."

Lillian thought for a few minutes and responded, "I guess I felt resistant because I've always been taught that to follow You I needed to become an evangelist and memorize my testimony in a way that I could dump on someone in an elevator. That just didn't feel like me."

Jesus smiled, touched her shoulder, and said, "Lillian, I call you to do what's natural to *you* and motivated by *your* heart. I do call some to be evangelists who proclaim my word boldly. But I call them, in that way, because it's how they're made. People make a mistake by trying to turn my giftings into programs for others. Life with me in my Kingdom becomes an adventure that I want to share with you. One day, in heaven, we'll celebrate together the amazing love and mercy of God with many people you've never even met, yet whose lives you've touched."

ഈഈ ൝൝

After Jim had paced the room and settled down a bit, Jesus continued, "Jim, you're basically on the right track at church, but only God can see the whole picture; what may look good to you might be the wrong thing or the wrong time for reasons you could never know." Jesus looked Jim in the eyes and said, "Jim, in the Kingdom of God, leadership really means followership. You don't have to be able to see and hear me physically to follow me; there's another way."

The discovery happened for Jim the next Monday at 3:45 P.M, as Jesus met with him in his office. Jesus listened for some time as Jim rehearsed the changes happening in his marriage and ministry. He exploded with joy about the new companion dog for Brian and the miracle of the anonymous money. "Did You arrange that?" he asked.

"Nope, had nothing to do with it."

"Really?" Jim retorted.

Jesus went on, "I guess I need to qualify that. In a certain way, I have something to do with everything. Whether or not I start something or permit something else, I could also stop those same things. Therefore I'm never really out of the loop, even in situations I detest." Jesus took advantage of the teachable moment, and continued, "But for your question to be answered, you have to understand how I operate as King of Kings. What do you think about that, Jim?"

Jim thought for some time and then responded, "That's really a good question; I should know, but I'm not sure." Thinking more out loud than giving an answer, Jim continued, "Well, You know everything about everybody and I guess you intervene in the natural course of events when You think it's necessary. Like sometimes You answer prayers in a big way and other times You seem to ignore them, or at least say no."

Jesus frowned. "Don't you think that would be pretty manipulative, Jim? That perspective makes Me appear more like the Greek "gods" than it does the God of Abraham, Isaac, and Jacob."

Jim repeated the word over in his head, "Manipulative." That's exactly the right word for how Jim had felt about God. Of course, he would never admit it, even to himself, but now that the word was on the table, Jim recognized his feeling. Even though he knew that God always has some greater purpose, answers to prayer seemed almost random. Bad things happen to good people and bad people alike. The Bible even says that.

Jim was about to admit his heresy when Jesus interrupted his thoughts and continued,

"First, there's no question about my authority and power. I could say to that mountain 'be uprooted and fly into the sea,' and it would obey Me. But I want my brothers and sisters to become co-heirs, not servants and slaves, with me in my Kingdom. If I just threw my power around, that's what I would make of you all. Manipulation does that to people; it enslaves them. You don't want to be treated like a puppet on the strings of an unpredictable puppet master, do you?" Jim shook his head, and Jesus finished His thought, "The Father and I designed a better way. Here's how it works, Jim. I exercise my Kingship in this world largely through adoption and transformation."

Jim wrinkled his brow. "Adoption and transformation? I don't get it. What does that have to do with whether or not You caused Brian to get his dog? You gotta unpack that a bit for me."

Jesus looked Jim in the eye and said, "If there's anyone who needs to understand this, Jim, it's an under-shepherd of my flock. Let me explain.

Jim poured another cup of coffee for the two of them and they settled back in their chairs. Jesus continued the unpacking. "Remember our early discussions about sin and forgiveness and the real meaning of abundant life?"

"Of course I remember! Those discussions felt like a laser-knife cutting away all my facades. I had understood all the words for a long time but had never really learned how to live in their reality. I think I'm beginning to experience the kind of abundant life you taught me – life based solely on Your love."

Jesus smiled and continued, "Remember that abundant life exists on two levels. I called them "two orders of my calling" on your life. Adoption happens as you answer Our first order call to live in Our love. But there's more to abundant life that you need to understand; you need to grasp My second order call."

Jim looked a bit confused and finally mumbled, "Go on."

"You understand adoption, Jim. The Gospel, the good news of my death and resurrection, invites everyone to repent of sin and rebellion, to accept forgiveness, and to believe in me. Adoption results." Jesus smiled, motioned to the Bible on the table, and said, "Open My Book, Jim. Turn to John 1:12 and read it out loud through verse 13." Jesus looked off into space and commented, "Did you ever think how ingeniously the early church fathers made it easy for us to study My Book by creating chapters and numbering verses? Imagine how hard this would be otherwise."

Jim hadn't thought about it actually. But he opened his Bible, found the place and began to read, "But as many as received Him, to them He gave the right to become children of God, even to those who believe in His name, who were born, not of blood nor of the will of the flesh nor of the will of man, but of God."

Jesus went on, "Everyone, since Adam and Eve's first rebellion, was born into sin, into bondage to damaged human nature, destined for death and eternal separation from Life. But, as you know, I came to redeem the world so that everyone might have life, and I give life to those who, in faith, receive the grace I offer. When a person receives this gift of my suffering and death on the cross, she or he becomes reborn as a daughter or son of God; the Father adopts that person. He also gives the Holy Spirit to those He adopts, so that they may become eternally connected to Us, become part of Our family, and help Us bring in the Kingdom of God. They're privileged to work with my Father and Me until We make all things new—the new heaven and earth." Jesus beamed as He thought about that new day and said, "It's the basic Gospel message, at least the first part. Isn't that wonderful, Jim?"

Jesus paused, and raising His finger, went on before Jim could respond, "But my brothers and sisters, even though filled with the Holy Spirit, still retain their God-given freedom to choose. Some choose well by following my leading, and some choose poorly by following themselves or others. Following me, as my adopted sons and daughters, happens when they exercise their free wills in ways that are consistent with mine. The Holy Spirit makes that possible by connecting our hearts in love. As I said before, we bring in the Kingdom together. So, returning to our original question about how I exercise my

Kingship, You see that much of what I do in the world is accomplished through my adopted family."

Jim reflected about what Jesus explained about the way He planned to get things accomplished in the world, and a sick feeling gripped him in the pit of his stomach. "Lord, I hate to say this, but that sounds terrible! You can't trust the Church to establish Your Kingdom; we're just not competent, not trustworthy, not…. his voice trailed off. "Why should we be able to do any better than the Israelites did? We're in trouble!"

Chapter 8: Transformation

Jesus sensed that Jim was getting tired and discouraged, so He suggested, "Let's take a break and continue this discussion later."

"You mean next week?"

"No, let's take a drive. I think a different setting will help us."

To Jim's amazement, Jesus motioned for them to leave the office. Jim locked the office door behind them and followed Jesus down the hall, through the Sanctuary, and out the front door. He locked the church door as he watched with almost horror as Jesus walked to Jim's car and stood on the passenger side, waiting for Jim to arrive and let Him in. "You're kidding," Jim stared wide eyed at Jesus. "What if someone sees us? What if I get asked who You are? What would I say? We can't be out in the open, can we?"

With a "give me a break" look on His face, Jesus motioned for Jim to unlock the door and get in. Jesus climbed in the passenger seat. Jim crawled in and just sat there. "Drive!" Jesus ordered. "Let me worry about getting seen. I've dealt with that problem before, you know, He said smiling. "Head down Main Street toward the highway."

Jim drove as he was instructed, wanting to duck every time someone passed by. Jesus seemed to enjoy looking at the town and the people walking and driving. He grinned as He watched children playing in their front yards. "I can remember when the Native Americans settled this land," Jesus commented, almost off hand.

"Where are we going, Boss?"

"I thought that the question forming in your mind back in your office might better be discussed from Fox Hill, overlooking the town. Might provide us a better perspective.

Jim drove down Main Street, onto the highway, and proceeded about two miles west. He then turned into the County Park and up the winding road to what the locals called their "mountain." Although Fox Hill stood only about five hundred feet above the level of the city, it did give a good view of Emmaus and the surrounding area. Jim pulled into the parking lot, picking a slot nearest the rim.

"Perfect," Jesus exclaimed. "Let's head over to those trees and find a place to sit."

Jim followed Jesus, who obviously knew where He was headed, into the trees at the edge of the hill. There, under a big oak, sat a small table sided by two wrought-iron benches. A red-checkered table cloth and two chocolate malts, filled to the brim of old fashion malt glasses complete with striped straws, adorned the table.

"You're kidding," Jim said again to Jesus.

"I told you that you'd have fun being my disciple, didn't I? What a great view! From here we can get a feel for the whole region. Have a seat."

Jim accepted the invitation, filled with amazement. Somehow the mystery about how Jesus set this all up rated right there with the multiplication of the loaves and fishes. Jim had to admit that he felt delighted. Clearly, Jesus enjoyed the whole thing. The two men sat quietly, sipping their malts, looking over the landscape. There before them lay the crisscross town of Emmaus with its courthouse tower, the central bank building, and the several church steeples, poking through a quilt of small houses with neatly trimmed lawns along tree-lined streets. Beyond the town, sprawled what looked like endless miles of planted fields dotted with white farm houses, red barns and blue silos. The afternoon sun joined with a scattering of billowy clouds to adorn the whole scene as though the heavenly hosts watched with them from above. Jim thought about all the people that lay hidden in that picturesque landscape and the pointless turmoil that filled the hearts of so many. "It is beautiful—at least on the surface" Jim whispered, slurping at his malt.

Jesus smiled at Jim and asked, "Now what were you going to ask before I launched us on this outing?"

Jim sat thoughtfully for several minutes and then responded, "I think I get the adoption part; could you tell me about transformation?"

"Glad you asked." Jesus smiled. "Let's use an analogy."

"Now you're sounding more like your biblical self," Jim quipped.

Jesus winked and continued, "Suppose you went to the poorest part of India or some other very poor country, saw a starving street child, adopted her, and brought her home. Would she immediately be able to take full advantage of living in your home and enjoying life as your daughter?"

Jim was about to say, "Sure," when he thought again. Actually, a similar thing had happened with a family in their town. They experienced real problems as their new daughter tried to adjust. So, Jim responded, "No, lots of things would have to change. She would have to learn English, learn to ask for food rather than steal it. A doctor would need to treat her maladies, like the parasites she's carried all her life. Becoming part of a new culture is no easy thing either. When you've been so abused, learning to be honest and trust others would take time and courage." Then Jim got the point, "She would have to undergo a huge transformation, wouldn't she? I think I get it."

"You've got it," Jesus said, clapping his hands and grinning. "I know you've memorized this, Jim, but take the Book and read the twelfth Chapter of Romans out loud, the first two verses."

At first, Jim felt panic. He hadn't brought his Bible from the office. He looked questioningly at Jesus who smiled and pointed at the lower shelf of the table. There lay a Bible, beautifully adorned with a leather cover engraved lettering, and hand painted images marking the beginning of the book and each chapter.

Jesus grinned at Jim's astonishment and said, "I think of things like this."

Jim found the reference in the Bible and read, "Therefore I urge you, brethren, by the mercies of God, to present your bodies a living and holy sacrifice, acceptable to God, which is your spiritual service of worship. And do not be conformed to this world, but be transformed by the renewing of your mind, so that you may prove what the will of God is, that which is good and acceptable and perfect."

Jesus went on, "My friend, Paul, personally understood what he wrote. Paul, himself, had to learn to trust my grace rather than some level of performance to the Law. He also worked with pagans who worshiped evil spirits and lived in a culture far from the supposedly humanitarian norms of today. He saw, as you have, Jim, that even though new believers were baptized with the Holy Spirit and contained within them the very power of God, they didn't know how to live like children of God or cooperate with their King in His great mission. They needed the transformation of a new identity, a new sense of security in my love, a new dependence on the Holy Spirit, new vision by seeing through my eyes, and a new strategy of life by following me."

Jesus paused, and then waved His arms toward the scene before them. "It's the same today. Your own statistics show that professed Christians live with about the same percentage of hang-ups and problems as non-Christians. In many cases, a church Elder Board meeting may not feel much different than a homeowners' association meeting in a local neighborhood." Jim could certainly relate to that analogy. Jesus continued, "It's because of a lack of personal transformation; people choose to act out of their broken patterns and expectations instead of choosing to follow a new way. Many believe, but they do not present themselves as a living and holy sacrifice. They don't surrender their old dependencies and identities and receive the transformation that I offer. Most don't understand how broken and wounded they've become until something challenges them to embrace radical change. It would be the same for our little Indian girl if she didn't recognize her need or refused to learn the new ways of her adopted family. But transformation takes much more than learning; the Holy Spirit transforms my adopted ones through a kind of open heart surgery."

"Open heart surgery?" Jim questioned.

Jesus stood up and paced in the grass in front of the table. "A lot of people have forgotten this last part, Jim. There's more to becoming a follower of Jesus, a child of God, than getting saved. That's the right start, but my brothers and sisters must use their own wills to really desire to become like me and to love and obey the Father the way I do. They have to want it! Only then can the Holy Spirit begin the process of transformation. As believers desire to experience the fruits of my life, and ask God for a new way of living, the Spirit begins renewing the damaged image of God within them, restoring the heart deformed by sin. This transformation process continues as people let go of their dependence on the world's ways and values and truly desire mine."

Jim's face lit up. He looked at Jesus and responded, "That's what's been happening to me these last weeks, isn't it? You showed me the false ways I've been trying to meet my needs by substituting the approval of others for the grace and freedom of Your love. I realized the pain it caused me and others and didn't want to live that way anymore. I hated that self-imposed tyranny. So, as I asked You to change me, desiring it with all my heart. The Holy Spirit did the surgery, the heart transplant, necessary to enable me to love You and trust that Your love makes me worthwhile. After all, I am your brother, a son of God!"

"Right on, Jim," replied Jesus, "and you didn't even need anesthesia for the operation!" They both laughed. "The transformation of the heart continues your whole lifetime. Remember that 'Only God is good.' You'll never become perfect in this world. Living in abundant life is not about 'getting to some level of perfection;' what's important, even vital, is that you're always in process, growing up, learning how to live in the abundant life you've been given."

Jesus stopped, faced Jim, and went on, "There's more, Jim. Another exciting part of this transformation happens as you live into your adoption."

"Wow," Jim exclaimed, "That seems like a lot to me already. What more could there be?"

At just that moment, a large red fox strolled into the clearing as though she didn't see the men sitting there. Her large bushy tail, tipped with black, fluffed behind her with a regal elegance. Jim stared with amazement as three young kits soon followed her into the sunlight. To his surprise, the mother fox rolled over on her back as the three kits attacked her furiously, growling and biting at her fur as though they would chew her to pieces. The mother responded to the onslaught just with a playful ferocity, grabbing the kits and tossing them off, chasing them around, then appearing defenseless to lure their repeated charges. Several times the foxes ran around Jesus and Jim, under the table and between the benches. Jim was almost certain that Jesus quickly put his hand out and patted a baby kit as it ran by. He watched with Jesus for several minutes and the battle raged, ending as the mother fox lay exhausted on the grass and her offspring snuggled up against her warm fur, laying on her back and neck. Then, as if on cue, the troop got up and trotted back into the woods.

Jim realized that his mouth had been hanging open, so he regained his composure and looked at Jesus. "What was that about?" he asked wide-eyed.

"Just a little demonstration that mother fox and I planned to illustrate the answer to your question! I told you this would be fun! You were asking what more could there be to transformation as part of your ongoing adoption experience."

Jesus grinned again. "It's a good question, one that most folks today don't ask. What was mother fox doing just now?"

"Playing, I guess."

"Oh, much more than that," Jesus responded. "Think about it some more."

Jim pictured the scene again, brightened, and offered, "She was teaching her kits to fight, to learn how to attack their prey so that someday they could hunt food."

"Exactly." It's the same thing that your Heavenly Father does for His kids, although a little differently. Let's use another adoption analogy that might be a bit closer to our situation. Picture a 'knights and kings' setting. The king of the realm rescues a young serf from a poor village destroyed by the king's enemies. The king takes the boy into his family, adopts him, and loves him as his own. The boy learns all the ways and manners of the court, becomes a good student, and lives faithfully with his new father. On his 18th birthday, the King presents his new son with a magic sword, one that can be used to conquer great evil." Jesus paused. "Get the picture?"

Jim, standing and gesticulating, picked up the story and continued, "So the time came when the evil hoards attacked the castle. The boy grabbed the sword and ran to battle. But he'd never learned to use the magic sword. He couldn't swing it or wield it properly, so he was overcome."

"Very good," replied Jesus with a grin. Then Jesus continued, "Now let's assume that the other knights did win the battle. Then they taught the adopted son to wield the sword with great expertise. Soon another enemy attacked again. As the castle is surrounded, the young man rushes into combat again. What happens?"

Jim was enjoying this lesson more than any of the others, and responded exuberantly, swinging his invisible sword at the nearby oak tree, "The boy wins the battle, of course."

"Wrong," replied Jesus. "Alas, the boy was overcome again."

Jim, now bewildered, responded, What? What's missing?"

"Oh, Jim, of all people, you should know. The young man, no matter how powerful, was only a small part of the king's army. He hadn't yet learned to fight in concert with the rest of the knights and most of all to follow the step-by-step instructions of the king."

"Of course," Jim replied somewhat dejected.

Jesus went on, "That's the Holy Spirit's role with knights of the Kingdom of God. The Spirit teaches you how to use the power of God with the gifts of the Spirit, and then He becomes the communication link with the Commander and Chief, the King. Remember Ephesians 6:10?"

Jim responded quickly and said, "I've got it." He went on to recite from memory, "Finally, be strong in the Lord and in the strength of His might. Put on the full armor of God, so that you will be able to stand firm against the schemes of the devil. For our struggle is not against flesh and blood, but against the rulers, against the powers, against the world forces of this darkness, against the spiritual forces of wickedness in the heavenly places. Therefore, take up the full armor of God, so that you will be able to resist in the evil day, and having done everything, to stand firm." Jesus motioned for him to continue. "Stand firm, therefore, having girded your loins with truth, and having put on the breastplate of righteousness, and having shod your feet with the preparation of the gospel of peace; in addition to all, taking up the shield of faith with which you will be able to extinguish all the flaming arrows of the evil one. And take the helmet of salvation, and the sword of the Spirit, which is the word of God. With all prayer and petition pray at all times in the Spirit…."

"Good. Now list these gifts of the Spirit as best you remember them."

Jim thought for a minute and then responded with a frown, "It would be easier if I could just read them." Jesus nodded, so Jim turned to Romans 12 and listed *prophecy, service, teaching, exhortation, giving, leadership, and mercy.* From 1 Corinthians 12, he read *word of wisdom, word of knowledge, faith, gifts of healing, working of miracles, prophecy, distinguishing of spirits, various kinds of tongues, interpretation of tongues.* Finally Jim turned to Ephesians 4 and listed the gifted roles or functions recorded there: *apostles, prophets, evangelists, pastors, and teachers.*

Walking and waving His hands as though Jesus were instructing a classroom of novice knights, He continued the lesson. "The Holy Spirit perfectly fits every regiment or body of believers with supernatural gifts which enable them to discern my leading and then follow me, using these gifts of the Spirit. You read about how I used them throughout the Gospel accounts of my ministry. The Apostles used them to win vast numbers with signs and wonders, and even raise people from the dead. Paul promoted their use in the churches to which he ministered, and James commanded healing in the church to which He wrote. You're given the gifts freely, but like the young knight, you have to learn how to use them and how to cooperate with me and with those who have other complementary gifts." Jesus paused to let Jim catch up.

"My knights have heavenly gifts to fight heavenly battles. That's the second part of transformation. The Holy Spirit teaches you how to discern the gifts He wants you to use at any given moment and at the same time tutors you about how to use them. When people see my love and power demonstrated in you, they will believe that I am present with you. Then, when they seek me personally, I will be found by them. It is simply what you pray in the prayer I taught you, 'Thy Kingdom come; Thy will be done, on earth as it is in heaven.'" Jesus sat back on his bench, smiled at Jim, "Okay, brother, I have downloaded a lot on you in this conversation. Why don't you summarize for us. What do we mean by adoption and transformation as the primary way I bring in my Kingdom and give you abundant life?"

Jim gulped, stood from the bench, and began, "Right. Let's see." Looking out over the town and imagining its people, he continued, "You work through people who have been adopted into your family and are being transformed into your likeness. Seems to me that it's a three step process. First, we're adopted when we receive You as our Lord and Savior and accept Your forgiveness for our sinful condition and acts." He took one step across the grass. "As adopted children of God, we gain all the rights, privileges, and responsibilities of your family. However, we have been deformed and wounded by our own sin, the world we live in, and the devil's schemes. We need the healing and equipping that will allow us to live out our new adopted identity. So, second," taking another big step, "Your Holy Spirit fills us with His presence and begins a heart transplant so that we can fully receive Your love and begin to love others. With this new heart like Yours, we can let go of our false gods and gain freedom from the demons that have ruled us. We, over our lifetimes, become transformed to become like You in our relationship with the Father and with others. That's the inward part of transformation." Jim took a third step and turning to Jesus, he almost whispered, "This is the part that scares me." Then he continued, "Third, the outward part of transformation takes place as the Holy Spirit teaches us to listen to Your leading and to use the spiritual gifts available to us in the community of other knights of the Kingdom." Jim sighed. "How's that?"

"I couldn't have summarized it better, myself, Jim!" Jesus beamed.

Jim looked relieved and grinned. "Thanks, Lord."

After a pause, Jesus leaned toward Jim and in a serious tone said, "My brother, you must instruct your people about adoption and transformation." He stood and opened His arms toward the town before them. "You must teach them what they need to know to live in my Kingdom and you must demonstrate how to do it."

Jim looked bewildered again, but Jesus pressed on. "You see now, Jim? Yes, I have overcome the world. I have won the final victory. But I have entrusted the battle for my beloveds into my children's hands, into your hands, Jim. You all have my wisdom and power available to you, the very Spirit of God; but they are your swords to wield. My followers write the history of this town, for better or worse. The extent to which I am recognized, known, and followed by the people of Emmaus stands largely up to you and the others here who know me. People will decide how they'll respond to your witness, but they can't respond unless they're at least exposed. I've entrusted my mission here to the Church of Emmaus."

Jim stood motionless, almost overcome by the weight of what Jesus had just taught him. As the sun lowered in the receding afternoon, the shadow of Fox Hill spread over Emmaus, adding to the gray uncertainty inside Jim. "It feels like such a huge task," Jim sighed. "That 'impossible' word keeps slipping back into my mind."

Jesus put his hand on Jim's shoulder and smiled. "It's actually exciting, Jim, when we do it together." Jesus embraced Jim with some comforting pats on the back. He then turned toward the woods and said over His shoulder, "We'll hold our next meeting in your office again, next Monday, but at 7:30 in the evening this time. Set a few more places; we'll be having some guests."

Jim glanced at the table, empty glasses, and benches. He heard Jesus' voice through the trees, "Don't worry, mother fox will take care of it!" He thought he heard a faint bark and some laughter.

৪৩৪৩ ৫৫৫৫

That week, Jesus met at the appointed times with Lillian and then Barry. To each He said, "This personal, face-to-face time has been precious to Me and you've learned and grown so much. I'm really proud of you. In fact, you've done so well, that I plan to adjust the way we meet for a while." Then He gave them each instructions about the next meeting's time and place. "The church will be open; just meet Me in the back."

They each responded with a wide-eyed, "What?" But Jesus had already disappeared.

Jim, Barry, and Lillian were more than nervous about whatever change might be coming in their meetings with Jesus. Those encounters with Jesus had been life-changing, to say the least. Now though, it seemed He planned to do something different and it made them uncomfortable. Jim, especially, felt almost frightened by the prospects of the next meeting. The previous rendezvouses with Jesus had been intense and personal. Their camaraderie had deepened; Jim felt comfortable even with Jesus' confrontations and challenges. He didn't want anything to change that.

At first Jim wondered about the ultimate purpose of these meetings with Jesus, but the question soon became lost in the wonder of it all. In this last meeting, particularly on Fox Hill, Jesus taught deeply and profoundly. Although the Scripture passages were well-known to Jim, he'd never been confronted by them, by Him in them, in such a powerful way.

A few nights later, Jim awoke abruptly in the middle of the night. Try as he would, he could not fall back to sleep. He got up, put on his robe, went into the library, and sat in silence. Brian's new dog came and put his head on Jim's lap. He reached for his Bible and began to recall the conversation. It all had started with Jim's inquiry about the dog. Jesus launched from a simple question into a profound lesson on Kingdom theology. "Amazing," he mused.

Jim pondered, "That's exactly the way the New Testament describes His conversations with people. He began with something simple and basic, like the need for people to get supper after a meeting so late on the mountainside. Then, five loaves and two fishes, and pow!" Jim returned to his review of

Jesus' lesson which started by questioning whether or not Jim understood how Jesus exercised His power and authority as King of Kings. He recalled the key words, "adoption and transformation." He reviewed the Scriptures in John 1:12-13, finding nothing really new about Jesus' offer of adoption as sons and daughters by God's grace received through faith in Jesus.

But he had never really thought about how difficult such a "cross-cultural" change would have to be. He thought about his own journey with God. Even though raised in a Christian home, he constantly struggled to live God's way instead of the world's way. Jim reflected, "It was a tough road at times, but I thought I'd done pretty well in becoming a believer, that is until Jesus showed me the basic motivation for much of my ministry." All these years and he still had so far to go. What would it take to actually think and feel like a child of God and become the image of Christ?

That thought took Jim on to the word "transformation." Jim grew up knowing that he needed to work hard at shaping up his life. As an athlete in high school, he'd learned how much training and work it took to perform to his capacity. Now as a Christian, he realized that the same determination would be needed to reflect the fruits of the Spirit rather than the fruits of the flesh. He turned to Colossians, the third chapter and read the well-known verses in Col 3:5, "Therefore consider the members of your earthly body as dead to immorality, impurity, passion, evil desire, and greed, which amounts to idolatry." The list seemed so starkly evil. Surely these things no longer posed a problem for him.

Jim's attention then turned to an investigation of each of the key words. As he reviewed each one, the Holy Spirit shockingly revealed their presence in his life. Immorality embodied anything less than the perfect good of God. Impurity described anything less than the purity of God and His love. In the word passion, he saw his desire for approval and success. Each word represented some aspect of real struggle in his life.

He read further into verse 10, "… put on the new self who is being renewed to a true knowledge according to the image of the One who created him…," and on through verse 17, "Let the peace of Christ rule in your hearts, to which indeed you were called in one body; and be thankful. Let the word of Christ richly dwell within you, with all wisdom, teaching, and admonishing one another with psalms and hymns and spiritual songs, singing with thankfulness in your hearts to God. Whatever you do in word or deed, do all in the name of the Lord Jesus, giving thanks through Him to God the Father."

As Jim pondered the passages, the words jumped out at him, "who is being renewed…." That reminded him of the transformation word and the passage in Romans 12. The truth Jesus taught him penetrated his heart and mind with vivid reality. "All these years I've been trying to make myself a better person, when I simply needed to surrender myself to the Holy Spirit and let Him renew and transform me." About the time Jim started to condemn himself for being so blind, he remembered Jesus' words, "You'll never become perfect in this world. Living in abundant life is not about 'getting to some level of perfection;' what's important, even vital, is that you're always in process, growing up, learning how to live in the abundant life you've been given." "Well, I guess there's still hope," Jim consoled himself.

Then his attention gravitated to the other aspect of transformation they discussed. "Not only do we have to become like Jesus in the way He relates to the Father and to others," Jim thought, "but we have to learn how to follow our King in bringing in the Kingdom." Jim had always recognized his responsibility to share the Gospel with others and invite them to receive God's grace for salvation. He understood his call to disciple new believers, teaching them to read the Scriptures, to pray, and to get involved in the life of the church. But he never really recognized his responsibility to actually make warriors of every believer, to help them mature, new and old. "I need to train them *how* to follow Jesus in their homes and workplaces and in their social relationships, not just tell them that they should." What troubled him most was that, in all his seminary training, no one had taught *him* how to do that either. "Hmm, Boot Camp for God's Warriors of Love. Sounds pretty intriguing. Would probably also get me fired." As Jim left the library, an uneasy question crossed his mind. "What in the world is He up to now? Why more chairs? I don't think I'm going to like this."

Chapter 9: Community of Light

Emmaus Community Church rested silently among the giant oaks, bathed in the yellow-orange sunset light, almost as if it knew that the next phase of Jesus' plan would rattle the lives of its members, if not its own hand-hewn stone foundation, and waited.

Thursday and 7:30 P.M. had come soon enough. Lillian, Jim, and Barry felt so nervous about this next meeting that they fidgeted all day. Why the church? Why a different time? Why more chairs? They knew Jesus had some sort of surprise in store, but couldn't imagine what it might be. It bothered them because it represented a change more than anything else. They had developed a sort of routine with Jesus. While the subjects of discussions were never predictable, Jesus was; He always interacted lovingly and kindly. Every meeting deepened their awareness of themselves and of God.

Barry never liked change in the first place, but messing with these personal "barn times" with Jesus felt unthinkable. "These hay bales have become almost holy!"

Lillian had found that the 5:30 A.M. times, both when Jesus showed Himself and when He didn't, had become the sure foundation and stabilizing factor of her busy life. She, like the others, knew that these personal visits with Jesus wouldn't continue forever, but they certainly weren't ready for them to stop.

Right after dinner, Jim headed over to church, arriving about an hour early. He told himself that he could use the time to work on his sermon. The truth, however, was that he was too nervous to do anything else. "What did Jesus mean by "Set a few more places; we'll be having some guests?" Was Jesus going to show up with Moses and Elijah?" He made sure his office was clean and put extra chairs in the room. Then he took a seat and waited.

Barry pulled into the church parking lot next, fifteen minutes early. He prided himself on never being late and enjoyed the one-up feeling of being the first one to arrive at a function. This time, however, he felt irritated that another car already inhabited the parking lot. He tried the door and, as predicted, it was unlocked. He went in. The Sanctuary glowed warmly, lit by the evening sun shining through the stained glass windows. The variegated colors spilled over the pews and across the Chancel. A mystical feeling filled the room and Barry wondered if Jesus might already be somewhere in the church. He waited.

Lillian sped into the church parking lot with only seconds to spare. She rushed up the church steps, threw open the door and almost catapulted into the room. She expected Jesus to be there tapping His foot, waiting for her. As the door closed behind her, she too was struck by the beautiful light that filled the church. She stood for a moment just taking it in, noticing the bright beams and the dark shadows. She also wondered if Jesus waited somewhere in the building, or would just appear and greet her. As she relaxed a bit and continued to survey the multicolored Sanctuary, her eyes fell on a form sitting in the last pew. She could tell at once it was not Jesus, however. Slowly Lillian walked forward until she could recognize....

As if on cue, Lillian exclaimed, "Barry?" and Barry, in the same questioning tone, "Lillian?"

Barry stood up and they both stared at each other speechless. "How could this happen?" each one thought, "I am supposed to meet with Jesus alone. This is supposed to be a secret. How am I going to get him/her out of here?"

Just when each was about to launch into some made up story about why the church Sanctuary was privately reserved, a familiar voice called out from one of the shadows at the front of the church, "Come in." Barry and Lillian both whirled around and saw Jesus kneeling in the front of the church. He got up, strolled toward them, and said, "The Father and I were just talking about this meeting."

Again, almost on cue, Lillian and Barry started to introduce the other, "Lord this is...." Jesus smiled and gave them both a hug. Dumbfounded, Barry and Lillian stood silently, both afraid to say anything that might betray the wonderful secret they'd been living.

"Follow Me," Jesus smiled, and led the way through the hallway to the end room and knocked on the door of Pastor Jim's office. Lillian and Barry starred at each other wide-eyed, still not saying anything.

They heard Jim's voice through the door, "Come in."

Jesus strolled into the room followed by his two guests. At this point it was Jim's jaw that hit the floor, as all three gaped at each other. Appearing not to notice, Jesus pointed each one to a chair and took His seat in the rocking chair. Speaking almost at once, Jim, Barry, and Lillian gasped out, "What? Have you...? What about the secret?"

Jesus interrupted and began the conversation as He usually did. "You all know each other," He smiled, "so we don't need introductions. Relax." He paused and then continued, "Your suspicions are correct. I have been meeting with each of you personally for several months now. We've had some wonderful times together, and I'm really pleased with each of you and your discoveries. What's happening in your lives makes a wonderful beginning. Now we're ready to go a bit further." Jim's, Lillian's, and Barry's heads swirled with confusion, grief, and dread as though they'd been suddenly catapulted onto an amusement ride that flung them in all directions at once.

Although the same question burned like hot spice on the tip of each of their tongues, Jim leaned forward in his chair, shyly raising his hand for permission to speak. Jesus nodded and Jim started, "But what about the 'no tell' clause?" The others, eyes wide and attentive, nodded.

Jesus grinned and responded, "Well, I suppose we'll need to amend that. Do I hear a motion?" No one said anything; in fact no one even moved. Jesus went on, "Let's change our agreement this way. You may never talk about our personal or group meetings to anyone, other than each other, ever. You may never refer or reference them when in the presence of someone else. Agreed?" The three faces, filled with astonishment and curiosity blended with fear and dread, nodded in agreement. "Good," smiled Jesus.

Jesus repositioned His chair so that He could look directly at all three. "Tonight we're beginning what you might call 'Phase Two' of what I want to teach you. In our previous meetings, we've been working on my personal relationship with each of you. You've come to know me in ways you never dreamed possible and learned more about yourself than you may have wanted to know. Believing in me means knowing me personally. I think that has happened for each of you." Jesus looked at them lovingly. They smiled and nodded, and Jesus continued, "Knowing Me has a wider dimension to it, however. You see, everyone who believes in me has become part of my family. And as a family, we live as believers together. In fact, it's the only way we live."

Jesus paused, rose from His chair, stepped toward the door, and said over His shoulder, "Hang tight while I get us something to drink. I think we have some dry mouths in the room."

While Jesus was gone, the silence felt deafening. In their minds, however, a rush of internal conversation flooded in. Jim thought, "Of any two in the church, these would be the last ones I'd have thought He'd meet with. Barry's always negative and hardly comes to church any more, and Lillian's always dour at Elder Board meetings and eager to get out of the room."

Barry silently grumbled, "Not this lame-leader pastor and this new half-committed elder. I'll bet there was a lot of real resistance going on in their meetings with Jesus."

Lillian's thoughts tracked much along the same line. "Now my personal times with Jesus are going to become business meetings with two men I sure wouldn't pick to meet with."

Jesus returned with a tray holding four cups of tea and a plate of cookies. He set them in the middle of the small coffee table and settled back in the rocking chair. Lillian, Barry, and Jim each awkwardly took a cup of tea and left the cookies on the plate.

Jesus smiled at the group and began, "I know none of you feel happy about this turn of events, but I want you to trust me. In time you will come to cherish the memories of these meetings as much as you have our personal visits. I know that you are not each other's favorites, but I chose you as a group for a reason that you will eventually come to understand. For the next several meetings we'll gather together as a group." All three breathed a sigh of relief. Although each of them disliked the new arrangement, they were also worried that this might be their last meeting with Jesus, and none of them felt ready for that.

Jesus continued, "I'd like to teach you about the family of God. I've never intended for any of my brothers and sisters to have to go it alone, in their faith, in their personal life, and never, ever, in following Me. My family consists of people who know, trust, and love me, and hopefully, one another. I know we're not there yet with the "one another" part, but let me lead and we'll see what happens. Have a cookie."

Jesus helped Himself and became preoccupied with putting just the right amount of milk and sugar in His tea, which surprisingly, had not gotten cold.

Jim broke the ice, "Barry, how are your boys doing? Did these late rains hurt your crops?"

Barry nodded, "May be tough getting the grain out of the field, but we'll get by; we always do."

Lillian quickly asked how Brian's new dog was working out, and Barry inquired about Lillian's kids.

Jesus passed the cookies around again and broke into the conversation, "I'd like each of you to tell the others about our first contact and early meetings. Tell it like it was. Jim, I'd like you to begin.

Jim fidgeted and coughed while Barry and Lillian sighed with relief. Jim went on to tell of that first night, of the vision, and his bewilderment. "I frankly didn't believe it was real. Who ever heard of Jesus telling someone to show up for a meeting? But with those conditions, I suppose we never would hear about it." Everyone chuckled. Jim went on, "The Lord," he shuddered, nodding toward Jesus, "was shrouded in light and I could make out a gold crown on His head. He told me that He knew about my frustrations and wanted to talk face to face. Then He told me the conditions—the same ones I guess He told you." Then he turned to Jesus, "I am so sorry, Lord, for being so skeptical, so unbelieving. It's amazing that You didn't chuck the whole thing." Then he turned to the others, "I'd been about ready to give up on Emmaus Church. I felt like such a failure because we weren't growing, as well as the financial struggles that took the focus off everything else. I'd become so skeptical and bitter that I even refused Jesus' offer of a hug at our first meeting. Can you imagine? I even felt kind of insulted when the King of Kings scheduled our next meeting at a time already booked on my calendar." The group laughed, and so did Jesus, and so did Jim. He continued, "I couldn't imagine that God would want to meet with a loser like me." The room went silent, Lillian and Barry appalled at the pastor's honesty.

Lillian cleared her throat and offered to go next.

"Great," Jesus responded.

"Actually, Jim, I could hardly wait to share because I think you got off easy. The Lord told me that I was so busy with my own life that He had to stage a hit-and-run to get my attention." Barry and Jim looked puzzled, and Lillian went on to explain how Jesus had stepped out from between two cars just when she had looked away. She shared about receiving the letter and the words spoken into her mind about being loved by God. Lillian described the contents of the letter, its invitation and conditions, and their first meeting at the coffee shop. "You weren't the only one who reacted skeptically, Jim. Even with all that happened, who could believe that the Son of God would want to meet in a coffee shop... with me!" She paused and went on, "I so wanted to believe that He really was Jesus and not some stalker. But why would Jesus want to meet with someone like me. On the outside I may have looked okay; inside I was a mess. However, He did seem to know what I'd been going through, even what I'd been praying. But I don't think I really believed it until I went home, unlocked the safe where I'd hidden the letter. The letter had disappeared just as He said it would." Then she turned to Jesus and said, "Thank You, Lord, for being so patient with me."

Jesus smiled, "I know you better than you know yourself, Lillian; I knew I could trust you. Thanks for your honesty."

The room fell quiet again as all eyes turned to Barry. He began, "I think I like the previous meeting arrangement better than this one. But if you want me to tell it, Lord, then I'll tell it." Barry went on to share about the first meeting, even the 'naked-in-the-shower' part. "Here's a man claiming to be Jesus with a towel over His arm like a butler. The disappearing thing was sort of flashy, but I wasn't convinced. I thought that Jesus only spoke to people through the Bible." Then he looked up at the group and grinned, "You know it's a lot safer that way!" They all laughed and knew how true it was.

Barry went on about meeting Jesus in the tractor that ran even with a broken part. He told them about Johnny, who

111

Jesus brought along to drive it. Tears filled Barry's eyes. "I knew right then that He was the Lord. I felt dumbfounded, couldn't say a word. We just plowed the field all morning together in silence. Just listening to that little boy laugh was enough to melt the devil's heart. From then until today, the Lord and I have been meeting in the barn, crack of dawn each week. A lot of healing's gone on in that barn."

Jesus looked at Barry and smiled, "Didn't think you could get beyond those wounds, did you Barry?"

Jesus looked at His watch and leaned forward. "Jim, is your office okay for us to meet in each week at the same time?" Before Jim could answer, Jesus said, "Great, I will see you all here. Remember, not a word, even to each other for now. Keep up the good work." Jesus gave them each a hug and walked out of the room.

Jim commented, "I could never figure out where He went after He turned the corner; there's no exit down that hall." Everyone laughed and filed out. Jim locked the church after them and they each drove home deep in thought. What in heaven's name would He want to talk about next time?

That week each of them pondered their meeting at church. They reflected on each person's sharing, amazed how Jesus had designed His initial personal introduction uniquely appropriate for each one of them. They thought about the skepticism with which each of them struggled. But they realized, at the heart of their disbelief, lay an underlying sense of self-degradation that found it almost impossible to believe that God would care enough about them to make such a thing happen. They wondered if most people would feel that way. How they, and probably everyone, underestimates Jesus' love for them. The Bible may say that each one of us is called by God, but who really believes it? They reflected about the ways they'd tried to live on their own, while professing to believe in Jesus.

Some significant insights came to Barry as he worked in the barn where he'd spent so much time with Jesus. "I can't believe the number of things I never prayed about! I assumed that Jesus was off somewhere doing more important things, and I only needed to try to get His attention for BIG issues like Elaine's death. It never occurred to me to ask Him about farming or my relationship with my kids."

Lillian commented to herself as she washed dishes, "I just assumed that it was up to me to be a parent, run a household, and love my husband. It's amazing that God wants to help and guide me with everything I do. I never even considered a partnership."

Jim had heard the word "under-shepherd" several times from Jesus. He reflected one day, "Can I really expect Jesus to be so aware of what I'm doing that He can become intimately involved? I've pictured God looking at me through a long-range telescope, getting the big picture. He only zoomed in for really big deals. All that changes with Jesus here, present. I'm not sure I know how to live in such an up-close way."

Another realization struck all three of them. They were amazed at how easily they opened up to one another. That couldn't have happened before these meetings with Jesus. They hadn't particularly liked each other in the first place, so sharing personal and sensitive issues would have been unthinkable. It seemed that the deep personal growth each had experienced, as well as the safety they felt with Jesus, enabled them to share vulnerably with one another. Each one wondered if there was a lot more to "believing in Jesus" than they yet knew.

Barry, Lillian, and Jim crossed paths several times that week, but they only nodded and walked on. To stop and talk would be out of the question. All their reflections and questions would flood out like a dam-burst and the wonderful adventure would evaporate. As their curiosity increased, it felt as though next Monday would never come.

Barry, then Lillian, then Jim arrived at the church, surprised to find the door already unlocked and the lights on. They entered and were again struck by the rainbow colors that bathed the Sanctuary through the stained glass windows.

Lillian guessed that Jesus chose that meeting time specifically for that reason. Not only were the colorful hues beautiful, but they invited her awareness into a reality beyond the room. The outside daylight appeared white; but in here, in the presence of Jesus, the light revealed itself as infinitely more complex, filled with depth and beauty beyond what the eye could see.

The three walked back to Jim's office and found Jesus there, with the chairs in place, the tea steaming, and what appeared to be fresh baked scones on a beautifully appointed tray adorned with fruit. "Come in and make yourselves at home," He said. "But remember that the rocking chair is mine." Jesus laughed and promptly took His seat.

This meeting immediately felt quite different from their first group time together. Their mutual comfort with each other went all but unnoticed because of their raging curiosity about what Jesus had in mind about getting them together. Then Jim noticed that there were two additional chairs in the room. He turned to Jesus and asked, "Are we having more guests? Have you been visiting more Emmaus people?"

Jesus smiled and replied, "As to more guests, the answer is yes and no. As to visiting more people, I guess that's my business." Jesus winked at Jim and went on. "I've brought two other chairs for the Father and the Holy Spirit. Actually, both have been present all along, and more involved in our conversations than you might have guessed. However, They don't sit in chairs the way I do, but the chairs can provide a reminder of Their presence and involvement." Jesus motioned toward the tea and scones, half bowing with hand outstretched. "I made these for you. I'm a great cook, if I do say so myself."

They helped themselves and fixed their tea. As they began to nibble on their scones, each one's eyes lit up. "They're cherry, my favorite!" exclaimed Jim.

Lillian took another bite, "I think it is coriander. I love coriander."

Barry frowned and said, "Come on, you're kidding. I know orange flavoring when I taste it. I've never had orange scones before. Delicious." They all stared questioningly at Jesus.

"You're all right, He explained. "I put all three flavors in the scones, but each of you have a pallet attuned to your favorite flavor. I made them that way because I want to please you, but there's a lesson in it that you'll see later. Now, let's just enjoy the scones and continue our conversation."

Lillian wanted to ask Jesus what flavor He tasted, but decided not to.

Jim automatically started to bow his head for an opening prayer, like he did for every church meeting. Then he thought," How ridiculous, God is right here, all three Persons of God!"

Jesus turned to Jim smiling and said, "Why is that ridiculous? Prayer is just conversation with US. What would you like to say?"

Jim felt a little awkward, but took Jesus' lead, "Well, I'd like to ask You to help us listen better to You, and to one another, and help us have the courage to be honest and open."

Jesus grinned and said, "Great prayer, Jim. The Father, the Spirit, and I want to do just that, and the fact that you want us to makes it possible. So, my first question: Does everyone else agree?" he asked the others. Barry and Lillian nodded. "You see, We want to help you and love you in every way, but we honor your freedom and won't force Ourselves upon you."

Leaning forward in His rocking chair, Jesus began, "Okay, here's what we'll do tonight, in addition to enjoying the scones, of course. I'd like each of you to share with the others what you've learned about yourself during our talks together. Share what you feel comfortable sharing, but tell the truth. When one of you speaks, the others are not to interrupt; just listen. Consider two objectives as you share. First, I want you to come to really know each other. Second, there is a part of each of your stories that's particularly relevant to each of the other's, something you and I haven't yet discussed. I'd like us to take the next three meetings for these discussions, with one of you sharing each night."

They all felt uncomfortable and grimaced. Where to start and what to say? Could the others be trusted? As they ruminated, Jesus spoke out, "Good questions, so let's put them on the table; it's much easier that way. First, you start wherever it comes to you to start and share what you feel is important. Remember that a part of your story will be particularly significant to at least one of the others." Jesus paused to let them consider what He'd said.

"The second question's also really important: Can you each be trusted with the heart of the others?" They looked thoughtful but didn't respond. Jesus went on, "Trust goes far beyond keeping a secret. You've each already pledged not to share what goes on among us. The question is, can you be trusted to listen with both your head and heart and not to judge the other person? It doesn't mean that you have to agree. But when you judge you ascribe a lower status to others, considering them less wise or holy than you. Nothing closes down the heart of another more than judging. Can you each be trusted to listen without judging?"

Barry was the first to respond, "Well, I can promise to try."

Jim interrupted, "Promising to TRY isn't good enough, Barry. I can only trust you if you DO it, not just try."

Jesus responded, "Barry, I'm glad you answered that way because you're exactly right. Trying is all you can promise to do. You can't control the thoughts that come into your minds or the feelings that emerge. However, TRYING means that you will reject judgments against one another when they arise. Jim, Lillian, does that make sense?" Both nodded their heads.

Jesus went on, "Remember the other two chairs. The one for my Father reminds us that only God can judge. Through my death He has already forgiven each of you and loves and accepts you as His sons and daughter. He judges or discerns, but He does not condemn you. We want to share His perspective toward others. The other chair will remind you that the Holy Spirit can help your trying. Remember that when I came to earth in Bethlehem, I had given up all my God-ship, and the powers that came with it. Only the power of the Holy Spirit enabled me to do what the Father asked, whether it involved talking and listening to people or performing miracles. The Holy Spirit wants to help you in the same way. You have very little power to actually act the way you want. But when you really want the power to be like me, and ask for it, the Holy Spirit who's present with you, actually in you, will help you. He abides with every brother and sister of mine, but few think to ask Him for help."

The group sat in silence, reflecting on what Jesus had said. Jesus finished his scone with a smile, put His tea and napkin back on the table, and stood up. "I'm sorry to have to leave the meeting early, but I have another engagement." The three looked aghast. Jesus quipped as He walked through the door, "But remember that I can be in more than one place at a time. Oh, and it happens that I'll have to let you share together for the next two weeks as well, without occupying my chair. I'll meet with you again on the third week, here at the same time." As He disappeared down the same dead-end hallway, they heard Him call back, "You'll do fine!"

Again silence engulfed the room, protecting the thoughts and feelings of its members. All three obviously felt disappointed that they were left together, *alone*. It would take real courage to be vulnerable without Jesus physically present in the room.

Barry was the first one to speak, again, "This stinks! I've never really opened up to anyone, even with Elaine or my boys. With Jesus, it's different. After a few meetings, I didn't feel embarrassed about what I felt or how I expressed things. I never attended college or learned a lot of fancy words. So, what I say is usually blunt and often not quite what I really mean, or at least not all of it."

Lillian chimed in, "I'm feeling really awkward, too. If it were anyone other than Jesus telling me to do this, I would have gotten up and just walked out. Not only is it hard to talk to strangers..." Lillian paused, and then went on, "Well, you're not really strangers; we've known each other for several years, and Jim you're my pastor. But we've never really talked. We don't know much about one another or our families and certainly not what's going on inside us. I talked with Jesus about really personal issues. I haven't even shared some of it with Walter, my husband."

Finally Jim joined the conversation, "I think I feel pretty much the same way. I've discovered some really personal insights that have made me a bit tender. So I have to admit I'm fearful about sharing with you. But Jesus asked us to share and I am not about to walk away from what He asked." The others raised their eyebrows and nodded, and Jim went on, "I have an idea. You're right, Lillian, we don't really know each other. It would be hard to put our conversations with Jesus into any real context. What if we begin tonight by telling our *pre-Jesus visit* stories, give some of our history and what's been going on lately—what life was like when Jesus made these radical visits." The room fell silent as they all pondered the suggestion, wondering if it would really make the task any easier.

Lillian objected, "But I thought Jesus told us to each take one night and share. I doubt that He'd approve of this change of plan."

"Yeah," Barry added. The group seemed stuck.

They were all deep in thought when Barry noticed it. "Look," he said quietly, pointing at the rocking chair, as it slowly rocked to and fro. As it rocked, it turned slightly toward the chair set aside for the Holy Spirit. Dumbfounded, they stared in silence.

Finally, Jim spoke up, "The Lord told me one day that the Holy Spirit connects us to the Father and the Son. Remember what Jesus just said about how we can't follow Him without the Holy Spirit? Let's ask the Spirit for help." The group started to bow their heads but then looked at the Holy Spirit chair.

Lillian verbalized the prayer for the group, "Holy Spirit, we want to do what Jesus asked, but it's really hard for us. We want to do this right; we want to please the Lord. Jim got this idea that would mean changing the schedule. Would you show us what to do?" The others nodded agreement.

As they sat together in silence, each one pondered the two alternatives: start sharing their Jesus insights now or begin with sharing their history tonight and start the Jesus insights the next week.

Lillian finally broke in, "I've noticed something and wonder if you're feeling the same thing. When I think of us just jumping in, I sense a kind of unsettled feeling. But when I imagine myself in the situation of sharing our life stories, then I feel more settled or comfortable. Does that make any sense?" Jim sat quietly, not wanting to sway the decision.

Barry responded after a few moments, "You're right. It began with your prayer, telling the Lord essentially 'not my will but yours.' Then, when I imagined starting with some history, it felt good. When I imagined one of us jumping right in, it felt wrong. What about you, Jim?"

Jim admitted that he had the same experience—feeling comfortable and at peace with the history alternative and uncomfortable with the jumping-in one. "I read somewhere that these feelings are called 'consolation and desolation'. The Holy Spirit brings consolation, but not desolation. Maybe this is one way the Holy Spirit guides us."

They had about an hour remaining for their meeting time, so they agreed that each of them would take twenty minutes. They reiterated the ground rules that Jesus had established. No repeating outside the room, no interrupting, and no judging.

Jim started, "Well, I guess I opened my big mouth about this, so I'd better step up." He went on to share where he grew up, his family situation, and his college years majoring in languages. He described the lack of affirmation he received from his family and his resulting need to prove to himself that he could really be somebody, making successful performance his source of security. He told about meeting Kate and falling in love, his call to seminary, and Brian's birth. Tears welled up as he shared the doctors' prognoses that Brian would live a difficult life if he lived long at all. Jim poured out his heart about his crushed dreams for a growing and impactful church and how difficult it had been to be a pastor at Emmaus. "As I told you last week, I think I was about done before Jesus showed up. It wouldn't have taken much and I would have left the ministry altogether." His twenty minutes were up, but he could easily have gone on.

Lillian and Barry looked at each other.

"You choose," Lillian suggested.

Barry somewhat whispered, "Don't think I have my courage up yet, why don't you go ahead."

So, Lillian began. Taking Jim's lead, she explained that she had grown up in Nebraska, not far from Emmaus, the eldest of two sisters and a late-arrival brother. She'd always felt pushed as the eldest and hurt by the favoritism paid to her brother. As soon as she graduated high school she left for college, just to get out of the house. Lillian confessed that although she grew up as a Christian, she sewed some wild oats in college and only after near disaster did she become involved with a campus Christian group. Although she majored in journalism, her dream had always been to live comfortably, get married, and raise a family. "Guess you'd say I wanted to be a typical suburban housewife."

Lillian told about meeting Walter a couple years after graduation, falling in love, and getting married. She described her two kids, Evan and Beth and what a delight they've been to her. Then Lillian turned to the more recent past. "I resisted the temptation to go to work to support the standard of living that Walt and I wanted because I couldn't stand the idea of leaving my kids, who are now 6 and 4, in daycare. When a better paying job opportunity opened up for Walt, however, I pressured him to take it, even though it meant he'd be gone most weekdays. Now I'm miserable having to run the house, parent the two kids, hauling Evan to this activity and that. My marriage is okay, I guess, but with Walter gone all the time, we're both too exhausted on weekends to have much of a quality relationship." She reported feeling fairly stable in her faith, but regretted agreeing to serve on the Elder Board. All of it together was just too much and she felt trapped.

With Lillian's twenty minutes over, Barry's turn arrived and he launched in faithfully. "There's not really much to tell. I was raised right here on the same farm I'm living on," he said flatly.

"Oh, come on," Jim and Lillian said almost in unison.

Barry went on to share the joys of farm life and how close he felt to God when his hands were in the dirt or the grain began to sprout. Barry, too, was the oldest child in his family, and like Lillian, resented being pushed and criticized about almost everything. "I learned to just work hard and shut up. It worked pretty well until I got married," he admitted. Barry told about his fears that he would end up a bachelor farmer and never enjoy a family. He hadn't gone to college and never really developed social skills. He reported that anytime he'd meet a girl, he'd do or say something stupid, feel embarrassed, and let the relationship drop. He went on to describe meeting Elaine and falling in love at first sight. "I would do the dumbest things and use all the wrong words, but something wouldn't let me stay away from her," he grinned. Barry shared about the birth of their boys and how his heart swelled with pride and joy. With tears he told about the discovery of Elaine's breast cancer, the years of ups and downs with chemotherapy, and finally her death just two years ago. "I lost everything. It broke my faith and I blamed God for letting me down. I was terrified of growing old all by myself, an angry and bitter man that no one could love. If Jesus hadn't come along...." his voice trailed off as his twenty minutes ended.

By this time all three of them were in tears. They stood, hugged, and said good night. The following two Thursday nights they met in the church office. They thought about asking one of them to make cookies or something and decided against it.

"Nothing like the ones Jesus makes," Barry quipped.

In the same order each one shared about their meetings with Jesus. They laughed together about his directness and matter-of-fact way of leading the conversation. They cried together as each one shared how Jesus had gone straight to the hidden wounds in their hearts, invited them to bring them into the light, and how He loved them in the very place of their brokenness. They also shared about the changes happening as a result of the new joy and freedom they were experiencing. Jim shared about renewed intimacy with Kate and the joy of Brian's new dog. Lillian told of her renewed love for Walt, describing ways Jesus had subtly shown her how to express her love to Walt and the kids. Barry told about meeting with the boys and their new attendance in church, but not a word about selling his cows and the gift to Pastor Jim. He never would, to anyone but Jesus, and Jesus already knew.

As they prepared to leave their third meeting, Jim spread out his arms as if to block the door. "There, we have done it again."

"Done what again?" the others asked.

"We've had a wonderful time together these last three weeks. But we ignored the Lord, at least I did. Somehow, I think we should have acknowledged the presence of the Father, Jesus, and the Holy Spirit. I feel like we ignored Them as silent witnesses to our discussions. No big questions came up, so we didn't need to ask for anything. But we didn't thank Them, either. God has done amazing miracles in each of our lives, and we just let Them sit here and ignored Them."

Then Lillian spoke up, "I didn't even think about it. How would I have felt if I'd been in one of those chairs, totally ignored? How could we do that, WE, of all people?"

Barry remained silent for a moment and then shared his perspective, "The trouble is we're all so used to thinking that They're up in the sky somewhere, looking down on us. We're not used to realizing Them in the room. Communicating directly came naturally when we could see Jesus physically. Even though He explained that He and the Father and the Holy Spirit would be in those chairs, we still forgot."

Lillian chimed in, "But we didn't do anything wrong, did we? I think we did pretty well at sharing the way the Lord wanted us to."

That's not the point," Jim responded. One of the important lessons the Lord taught me was that He is our Shepherd and wants to lead us personally. It's not so much doing something wrong, but of being attentive to the fact that God is with us, communicating with us."

Lillian piped up, "That reminds me. Jesus said that there would be some key part of each of our stories that would act as a special message to one or the other of us. We didn't even talk about that."

Barry mused, "I wonder if that was something we should have been asking the Holy Spirit to show us?" The group fell quiet again.

Then Jim spoke, "Well, all is not lost. Jesus said that He would never leave us or forsake us. God is with us in this coming week before our next meeting with Jesus. Let's ask Them right now to help us recognize what we missed." Lillian and Barry nodded.

They sat down again and looked directly at the three chairs. Barry began, "Father, forgive us for these lame habits. We want to honor You as our Heavenly Father by loving You as one of Your kids. Please help us to live our lives with You, not ignoring You."

Lillian went on, "Jesus, I ask Your forgiveness, too, for ignoring what You told us to do. We talked and shared just like You were off on some other business. We're so sorry. Thank You for what You're doing in our lives. It's still hard to believe that You love us so much that You're always with us. Lord, we now realize that by ignoring You we've missed a vital part of what You've designed for us. But we trust You to help us, even now."

Jim completed the prayer, "Holy Spirit, in the name of our Father God, and of our Lord Jesus, we humbly ask You to help us complete our assignment. In the coming week would You please help us recall our conversations and show us what we've missed. Thank You for helping us really open up and share and even learn to love each other. We trust You to show us what we need to see. Thank You, Father, Jesus, and Holy Spirit. Amen"

Tears ran down their cheeks as they shared hugs, and Lillian whispered, "Will we ever learn?"

During the following week, each of them spent focused time daily recalling the conversations from the previous Thursday nights. Each one began their time addressing their Heavenly Father, Jesus, and the Holy Spirit. They expressed their prayers similarly: "Teach me, O Lord, to know Your ways and to recognize Your voice within my heart."

Lillian sat silently each morning at 5:30 A.M. Jim did the same in his office at 3:30 P.M. Sunrise found Barry sitting on that same bale of hay. All listened to God and to their own hearts.

The next Thursday evening finally came, and all three met in Jim's office at church. Jesus arrived last, grinning as He presented the tea and scones. "Thought you'd like to try these again." Plopping in the rocking chair, He began. "I couldn't be more pleased with each of you," He beamed. "You followed my instructions and when the Holy Spirit prompted Jim to suggest something that would make it easier, you checked it out and followed your hearts' leading. You listened attentively, kept confidence, and didn't judge. You opened your hearts and learned to love one another. You've formed the beginnings of a community of light, something like the Father and Spirit and I have. I am really pleased."

Barry interrupted, "But, but what about ignoring You in our meetings and forgetting to ask the Holy Spirit to show us what we were supposed to hear in one another's stories? We blew that big time. We're all really sorry."

Jesus smiled at Barry, "But you caught yourselves and made it right. Yes, you blew it, but more importantly, you learned from your error. The best part shines in how you went forward from there. You knew what you had to do and Who would guide and empower you. Then you asked humbly and thankfully. I really am proud of you."

Looking each one in the eye, He went on, "You see, I'm not hurt or even disappointed when you make a mistake. That's just part of learning. I'm disappointed when people don't learn from their mistakes."

Lillian picked up the plate of warm scones and passed them around. Jesus took one, lathered it with butter, took a bite, and with his mouth full, mumbled, "Well, let's continue with our conversation for tonight. Tell me what you learned from your experience and what you spotted in one another that spoke to your own heart."

Almost talking at once, they related their surprise at the depth of trust that developed and their awareness that could never have happened if Jesus hadn't already accomplished significant healing in each of their lives. Each one expressed how much they felt blessed and somehow released through sharing with the group.

Lillian put it this way, "Jesus, I thought that sharing my heart with You and having Your love and acceptance provided more than I could ever want. But I was surprised at the additional level of joy and insight I experienced by sharing it all with Jim and Barry. I guess I expected You to understand and care, but when they received and affirmed me as well, it felt like a patch of light glowed in my heart and in this shadowy town of Emmaus."

Jesus responded, "That's a very accurate analogy, Lillian. You see, together we're to be a community of Light, My kind of Light. Even though you've met with me separately, you now have discovered that living life together in a community of truth, trust, and love provides a place of safety, health, and strength. The Father and I designed humankind for that kind of community, the kind that the Father and the Spirit and I share. You're created in Our image. That's why I said to my disciples that where two or three are gathered together in my name, I'm right there in their midst. Of course I'm with you individually, but you experience my presence more fully when you're together in my name, depending on my presence."

Jim commented, "I think we feel just like your biblical disciples, sitting with you on some hillside, listening to Your teaching. This couldn't be more exciting!" The others nodded broad smiles.

"Your advantage," Jesus responded, "is that you have the New Testament and the Holy Spirit to help you understand what I am saying. My twelve really struggled."

"Okay, let's get to the topic for tonight. In discussing that, I'm going to teach you an important lesson about spiritual community. I want you to understand it both by hearing me teach, and by experiencing its reality." Jesus paused as though to let His audience gather their full attention.

"Have you noticed how often you, and most of my followers, ask 'why' in their prayers? Have you also noticed how seldom I answer that question? There's an important lesson here. When the Father, the Spirit, and I choose a course of action, it's designed to accomplish a myriad of purposes and blessings. There's no 'one' reason for Our plans. In fact, more reasons and consequences exist than you could possibly understand. Someday you'll be able to see them from the perspective of heaven, but not from here.

"I want to demonstrate what I'm teaching you through looking at our recent experiences together. You've each been wondering why I appeared to you. Further, you've wondered why I brought you together. You've experienced some amazing results from our visits—results in your own lives, in your personal relationships, in your church, and now in your relationships with one another. But there's more happening than you can see, much, much, more."

He turned first to Lillian. "Lil, how did I speak into your life through these brothers?" Lillian had already thought it through and was ready.

"I don't know if I've gotten it all, but in reflecting on Jim's and Barry's stories, I recognized a common theme in which I could see myself. I realized that all three of us grew up with unreasonable expectations placed on us, often through negative prompting and criticism. Our parenting was skewed. I now see that I've projected that upbringing on our Heavenly Father and on You, Lord. In my mind, I conformed You to my image. So, to a large degree, I put myself between the lose-lose positions of trying desperately to measure up on the one hand, and not accepting the love and affirmation that You freely offer me on the other. I'm realizing that the only way I can really love others in action is to let Your love flow through me. But I'm finding that receiving Your love proves harder than I'd imagined. I need You to teach me how to be parented by the Father and led by You. I've also realized that I need to forgive my parents for not being perfect parents."

Jesus looked lovingly at Lillian, "You heard correctly, Lillian. It's very common for people to project attributes of their human parents onto God, but it's seldom recognized. No one grows up with perfect parents, so they always relate to God through some misperception of His nature. However, when the Holy Spirit reveals these faulty views of God you gain a wonderful new opportunity. You can repent and ask Us to help you relate to Us as We really exist. You've come to know more of yourself, Lillian, and grown to become more of your true self. It's my pleasure to teach you how to know the Father and receive His love." Lillian's and Jesus' smiles at one another beamed with love and excitement. Lillian felt almost giddy imagining what life like that would be like.

Jesus turned to Barry, 'Okay, tiller of my Father's soil, how did I speak into your life through your brother and sister?"

Barry described what had come to him in his hay-bale sitting this last week through Jim's story about his son, Brian. "Once I heard what it takes to parent a special needs boy, I could only imagine the patience needed. Patience has never been my long suit. My dad was impatient with me and I acted the same way with my boys. Like Lillian, I always felt that You were impatient with me, and I resented You for it. When Elaine died, I felt that You were punishing me for not being good enough. I also took my anger and impatience out on others, particularly you, Pastor Jim. You somehow represented God, and I resented that God seemed to approve of you, but not me." He looked at Jesus and then at Jim, "Would you both please forgive me? Lillian, please forgive me for the impatience and hostility I've shown on the Elder Board." All three nodded with an understanding smile, then stood and warmly hugged Barry.

They sat in silence for a time, and then Jesus looked at Jim and grinned, "Well, you're up, preacher. What did you learn?"

Jim turned to Lillian and said, "As far as I could tell, God used you as a mirror to help me see myself. As you talked about your frantic life, managing your home and children with your husband gone, I could see myself. I've frantically tried to run the church and keep all the balls in the air. Just like you, I expected success but was too busy to seek help from others and especially from You, Lord. I acted like a homemaker without a husband, I guess. I realized that Your church is the Bride of Christ, and You, Lord, are her Husband. In my pride and stupidity, I've tried to husband Your church and then expect You to bless what I do. When You didn't do what I wanted, I angrily blamed You. It would never have crossed my mind that You sent Barry and Lillian into this church to help me. My ego deceived me into thinking that only I could do things well enough, and so I ignored the community You brought together. This may sound funny, Lord, but I realize that I need to learn how to be a Godly wife. Now I have a clue about why You compared, in the book of Ephesians, the marriage relationship between a husband and wife to Your relationship with the church. I'm so sorry. Would You teach me, Lord? Barry, Lillian, would you forgive me and help me?"

Jesus stood up and motioned for them to come closer. He spread out his arms and beamed with pride. "You've all listened well. You have listened to me, to your own heart, and to one another. I told my first disciples that my sheep recognize my voice. That's the way you hear my voice. What you learn in My Book becomes alive to you as I show you its truth in your own heart, in the lives of others, and through the whisper of the Holy Spirit. I think you're all doing wonderfully."

Jesus paused and then continued, "But there's another essential part of living as my community, which may be the hardest. Meet me next week, same place, same time." Jesus' expression had turned more somber, and the three wondered what would come next.

Chapter 10: The Church

The next Thursday evening found Jim, Barry, and Lillian gathered in the church office. Their gatherings took some work to disguise. The three couldn't lie about what they were doing, but at the same time, they couldn't just tell people that they were having a rendezvous with the Messiah, either. Most of the church members recognized their cars parked in the church parking lot. Few secrets existed in Emmaus.

Jim had told Kate that he was meeting for some elder reconciliation and couldn't discuss it because of confidentiality. Kate felt curious, however, as Jim usually acted pensive and quiet after these meetings. Lillian had to hire a sitter each Thursday evening, so it was obvious she was out. She was able to tell Walt simply that she had a meeting at church, and that was fine with him. He was usually gone on Thursday nights anyway. People were used to Barry's tight lips about what he did, so no one asked him what was going on at church every Thursday night.

Jesus arrived with His multi-flavored scones and tea, and the group settled down to the discussion. They'd been curious about what Jesus might bring up, as His tone last week suggested the subject might take a different turn. Sure enough, it did.

Jesus began, "I couldn't be more delighted by the times we have spent together."

Lillian cut Him off, "You don't mean that our meetings are going to come to a close, do you?"

Jesus smiled, "It will have to happen one of these days; but no, we still have some important ground to cover—maybe the most important ground yet." The three swallowed their mouthfuls of scone and looked at Jesus attentively. Jesus leaned forward in his rocking chair and began, "None of you have asked why I picked you to visit in the first place, and why you all happened to go to the same church, but you've been wondering." The three heads nodded and they grew even more focused.

Jesus went on, "I want to talk to you about how you do church—the way Emmaus, and other churches, conduct their life as the Body of Christ. Some things have started to change a little at Emmaus since we've been meeting, but I'd like to put the subject on the table and discuss it together. Let's start by asking each of you what you like most about Emmaus Community Church."

Jim knew he had to go last, so he sat quietly and pretended to be deep in thought. Barry and Lillian sat for several moments and finally Lillian volunteered to go first.

"Well, I like lots of things about our church, so I'm not sure where to start. First, I don't feel I fit in the other churches in town, so that's why I'm here. I like your messages, Jim. They're biblically based and always thoughtful. There's usually a point that I can take home and mull over. I like the choir and the music we sing, and I like the fact that we support foreign missionaries. It's special when they come home and share in church. I really enjoy hearing what God does in other parts of the world. Oh yes, and my kids really like the Sunday school. They always show me something they've made during class."

Jesus smiled at Lillian, "Thanks, Lillian. Barry, what do you like?"

Barry, ready by this time, jumped right in, "Pastor's sermons are okay, but sometimes a bit over my head. I like the music, too, and people here are friendly to one another and to visitors. The missions program accomplishes a lot, and I appreciate all the volunteers who work with our kids. We have to invest in the next generation, you know."

"Thanks, Barry," Jesus responded. Jim, you're up."

Jim cleared his throat and began, "First, I have to admit that I am sort of a perfectionist, so I usually focus more on what needs to be improved. So this is a little hard for me. I like to preach and seem to get pretty good feedback on my messages. I enjoy teaching, even for the few who turn out for adult Sunday school. I'm glad that we receive visitors, too, although I don't think we do a very good job of getting them involved."

"On the positive side," Jesus coached.

"Sorry. I'm with both of you; I like supporting missionary families. I think we get a real taste for the rest of the world that way. Jim paused for a while, "Guess that's enough for now."

Jesus looked at the group and said, "Okay, what don't you like? Let's go in the same order to keep it simple. Lillian?"

Lillian glanced at Jim with an embarrassed smile. "Well, I don't like to be negative, and I'm sure I couldn't do any better, but I hate most our Elder Board meetings. They feel like my homeowner association meeting, always dwelling on the negative. Sometimes, when I'm driving home after one of those meetings, I want to quit the Board and even the church. Why do people have to get so tense and angry? We're supposed to love one another. I guess there's another thing that bothers me. I think that our church seems pretty much irrelevant to the people of Emmaus. We're an institution that everyone knows about, but I don't think we really make a difference in our community. When's the last time we brought someone into the church that wasn't already a Christian and hadn't moved here from somewhere else?" Lillian sighed and sat back in her chair.

"I appreciate your honesty, Lillian," Jesus said. Barry, what bugs you about this church?

Barry complained, "We're not growing. Giving is down. Why, if people in this church would give even five percent, we'd be doing fine. If they would tithe like they're supposed to, we could really accomplish things. People aren't committed. It's hard to get volunteers; same old group does everything. I hate to say this, Pastor Jim, but I think it's a matter of leadership. There's no vision, no reason to give other than to keep the machinery working. Your sermons are okay, but they sure don't motivate people. Sorry, Pastor. Finally, I guess I have to agree with Lillian that this church doesn't make any difference in the community or in other people's lives. They just see us as a social club filled with judgmental religious hypocrites." Barry looked apologetically at Jim.

Jesus spoke up, "That's okay, Barry. Don't apologize. I asked your opinion, and we all appreciate your honesty." Jim and Lillian nodded. Jesus now looked at Jim.

Jim looked a little haggard, and began, "Well, like I said, I tend to look at what needs to be done better, so I suppose I could mention most everything we do. But I'm with you, Barry. I'm discouraged with most of the congregation's ho-hum attitude. I agree that my sermons aren't setting any fires under people. Hopefully they're learning something, but it isn't showing up in their giving or participation. Lillian, I'm with you, too. I don't see us impacting our community the way we should. I don't like the Elder Board meetings any more than you. I dread them all week and then can't sleep the night after. You may be right about the leadership, Barry. And maybe you're right about how people see our church."

Jesus put his hand on Jim's shoulder and responded, "You're working hard, Jim. Some good things happen at Emmaus, like you all pointed out. But, Jim and Barry, you're both right. There's a problem with leadership, but it's not just Jim's fault."

The group sat silently for some time. In all their personal times with Jesus, they'd managed not to talk about the church. In the group meetings, the church had only come up in Jim's sharing, but no one had responded. The meetings had been filled with deep emotion, healing, honesty and friendship, and usually a lot of laughter. But now a dark cloud seemed to hover over the group. Barry and Lillian felt sorry for Jim, and they all wished the topic could have been avoided.

Jesus broke the silence. "Like I said, some really good things happen through the ministry here. But I'd like to talk to you about this issue of leadership. Jim, Barry, Lillian, this is my church. I birthed it; I called the people to it; I have dreams and visions for her role in people's lives and the coming of My Kingdom." The group hardly breathed, as Jesus went on. "The trouble is, the people conduct the affairs of the church, for the most part, as though I weren't here." Jesus let the statement hang in air. In all their conversations with Jesus, this was the first time He had expressed displeasure, and the three felt a gravity and discomfort they'd never felt in their previous visits with Jesus.

"Let me give you some examples," Jesus continued. "In most Sunday morning church services, people behave more like they're attending a memorial service to a historical figure than participating in an opportunity to be together with me. You sing songs about me, teach about me from the Bible, take up an offering that goes more for buildings and the utility bills than it goes for my work. While prayers occasionally get addressed to me, many times they're mini-sermons to the congregation. In either case, people often imagine me somewhere up in heaven, possibly watching, but not really involved."

A dismal cloud hung over the group as they realized the truth of Jesus' words. Jesus went on, "You all mentioned your dislike of the Elder Board, the leadership group for Emmaus Church. Do you think things would go differently if I were sitting physically in the room? Like the church service, those meeting go on as though I were not the Leader of the church at all, as though I weren't even present. Usually, the only time I'm mentioned is in the opening and closing prayer. The Board usually determines the agenda without asking me what ought to be on it. You go through each agenda item, sharing your own thoughts and opinions, but never asking me what I think. Decisions are made using only your own limited knowledge, mostly with good intentions, but usually based on a flawed understanding of reality. Many times you tell others what you think they want to hear or maneuver to get your own way, never remembering that I'm in the room, knowing every thought. Then you close with a prayer to some idea you have of me, up in heaven, safely out of reach, to ask this far-away Deity to bless your plans. When things don't work out as you expected, you blame some other person in the group, most often Pastor Jim."

Again the room was silent. Jesus spoke so directly and specifically. Lillian wondered why Jesus didn't use some sort of parable to soften the blow. Jesus sat in the rocking chair with a concerned look, and each of the three could have cried. Jesus went on, "I know you each believe in me and want to do the right thing, but you've copied the organizations of this world. The systems of this world have molded the church in their own image and the prince of this world has clouded your vision. Emmaus Church has become an institution more about its members than me. It behaves more like a club for insiders rather than a rescue mission for the lost of the world, concerned with pleasing itself and its members rather than me. Instead of heralding the truth that I am alive and present, offering abundant life to everyone, the church gives the impression that I offer judgment rather than life, that I'm irrelevant to their lives, and that I don't care enough about them to be present."

Jesus paused and His tone softened, "I know that's not what you want to do, or even realize you're doing, but you know it's the truth. Based on your experience of our meetings together, you can see that what I'm saying is true. Why did it take my physical appearance to evoke such change in you? Would you want your lives to be the way they were before you came to know me in the flesh? No, of course not." The three shook their heads and Jesus concluded, "What has happened to you, through the experience of my presence, demonstrates what I want to happen to the world around you. Just as it did with you, it must come about through my presence in them."

After a long silence, Jim spoke up. Speaking for the group, he said, "Lord, You're right. Our lives have changed so dramatically since coming to really know You. The church faces the same trouble we faced. We didn't comprehend how to know and love You before, because it actually did feel as though You were somewhere up in heaven. Now that we've experienced You as Presence, we can see the truth of what You're saying about the church. But we still have the same problem. We don't know how to do what You're asking. I don't know how to do what You're asking." Jim's tone expressed his exasperation and Lillian and Barry's expressions signaled their agreement.

Finally Jesus smiled at the group, although not with one of their favorite broad grins, but a sympathetic warm look that said, "I understand." Jesus got up from his rocker and the others stood. "I know you don't know how to accomplish what I desire for my church. You're not alone; most don't. But my question is this: Do you <u>want</u> to know? Are you willing to learn?"

Again, silence. The feeling in the room took on an air of importance, even urgency, as though all the heavenly beings waited for their answer, and maybe wondering, "How did these three nobodies from a nowhere town come to be standing in the presence of the King of Kings being asked to make this choice? Even if they learned to lead the church the way Jesus wanted, what difference would it make in a place like Emmaus?"

Jim finally responded for the group, "Our hearts have burned with love since You've met us in this way. We do want this for others, but we have no idea how to do it. Lord, please teach us." The four hugged and wept. Never before had the three felt such love, yet such a challenge.

Jesus smiled again at them. "Good. I hoped you would want to follow me. But it's going to take some preparation.

During the next two weeks before we meet again, I have two assignments for you. First, I want each of you to spend time visiting the people in this town, the people who don't go to church, the people who don't believe, the people trapped in the systems of this world, the hopeless—rich, middle class, and poor. I want you to visit those who are down and out. They may be more hidden in a rural community than in an inner city, but people know who they are. Look for them at the shelter, on the streets, under bridges, and at the state hospital. Locate the widows and widowers. Go to the bars and taverns. Get to know the rest of the people I went to the cross for."

As if that weren't enough, Jesus stood and continued, "My second assignment is for your next Thursday meeting. Jim, I want you to share with the others what I taught you about adoption and transformation. You journaled it when you got home and those notes will do just fine as an outline. Once you've all gotten to know my people, you share with Lillian and Barry what I want to do for them. Then I'll see all of you two Thursdays from tonight – same time, same place." Jesus smiled, turned the corner, and was gone.

Jim said to the others, "Can we stay for just a minute and discuss our assignment?"

As they took their chairs, Lillian spoke up. "I feel terrible," she said. "He's absolutely right about the church being all about me. I feel like such a blind and selfish person."

Barry picked up the theme, "He nailed me about the Elder Board, too. All I was concerned about was getting my own way. I thought I knew how a church should be run. It never occurred to me that I was trying to push Jesus out of the way."

Jim followed, "I know how you feel and believe me, I feel the same way. I've seen myself as a failure for years, but never for the right reasons. I thought I should be smart enough, with seminary and all, to lead this church. Sure I depended on Jesus, but I expected Him to do what I wanted, to honor my dreams. I never asked Him about His dreams, specifically for our church." Again the room fell silent—even dismal.

But Lillian spoke up, "Let's not get too down on ourselves. We know that Jesus didn't come to condemn us or make us feel bad. He came to help us, and somehow, I think He's offered us something very special in His plan for the Kingdom of God."

They stayed for another hour, discussing their strategy for meeting the people Jesus had mentioned. Each knew several personally. Jim told them who to contact at the local shelter. They compiled a list of widows and widowers and agreed on who should visit whom. They agreed to go together when they visited the local pubs.

Barry commented as they were leaving for home, "Hey, and don't forget to ask the Lord who to listen to and what to say. He told us He would be with us. Let's not ignore His Presence this time." They all nodded and smiled. Driving home, each one talked to the Lord sitting in the passenger seat, even though they couldn't see Him. More confession, more expressions of gratitude, and a lot of requests for wisdom and help filled their time.

As he pulled the car into the garage, Barry recalled Psalm 86, "Teach me Your way, O LORD; I will walk in Your truth; unite my heart to fear Your name. I will give thanks to You, O Lord my God, with all my heart, and will glorify Your name forever. For Your loving kindness toward me is great, and You have delivered my soul from the depths of Sheol."

When Lillian returned home, she glanced at the devotional calendar that sat on her kitchen counter. It quoted Psalm 143, verses 10 to 12, "Teach me to do Your will, for You are my God; let Your good Spirit lead me on level ground. For the sake of Your name, O LORD, revive me. In Your righteousness bring my soul out of trouble. And in Your loving kindness, cut off my enemies and destroy all those who afflict my soul, for I am Your servant."

Sitting in his recliner at home, Jim recalled the passage from Jeremiah chapter 29, read at his ordination: "For I know the plans that I have for you,' declares the LORD, 'plans for welfare and not for calamity to give you a future and a hope. Then you will call upon Me and come and pray to Me, and I will listen to you. You will seek Me and find Me when you search for Me with all your heart. I will be found by you,' declares the Lord...."

Each emailed the others with the passages the Lord had given them, with words of encouragement and hope.

That week and part of the next, each of them made their visits. They agreed to introduce themselves as Elders from Emmaus, trying to get to know their town better. They promised that all they wanted to do was listen. They wouldn't try to get the people they visited to come to church or give them any religious material.

Barry asked to visit the widows and widowers in the extended farming community. He would call and ask to stop by for coffee. A respected farmer in the area, he was seldom refused. In farm homes and the care facilities, he listened to women and men whose hearts had been broken by the loss of their mates. He understood their feelings when person after person told him that a very part of their heart had been ripped out of them. Now, needing community more than ever, they felt out of place in a couple-dominated culture. It hadn't been too long after the funerals that people pretty well left the bereaved to themselves – alone. Some of the newly-widowed felt comforted by their faith, but more blamed God for taking their loved one. "If only I could explain it like Jesus did," Barry thought to himself. But he was only there to listen.

Barry had also agreed to visit the bars with Jim and Lillian. Barry called himself a teetotaler both by choice and necessity. Soon after his marriage to Elaine, he'd realized that alcohol enhanced his already impatient and brusque character. Following Elaine's death, he recognized pretty quickly how easily he could drown his sorrows in booze. He was surprised at how many people he recognized in the local bars. One neighboring farmer scoffed at him, "What are you doing here? Come to look down on us drinking folks?"

Barry replied almost without thinking, "No, I've realized how judgmental I've been. Just because I can't drink, I've looked down on others who do. I'm sorry and want to make it right. Mind if I have a Coke with you while you have your beer?" The neighbor welcomed him in as Barry met a number of his neighbors and others he didn't know. Some came to the bar just to meet friends and others showed up because they thought they needed a drink. Many felt judged and excluded from the church. Barry listened to their stories and laughed at their jokes and even told a few himself.

Later, as Barry, Lillian, and Jim processed their tavern experiences, they wondered if more fellowship existed at the bar than at church. Certainly, the drinking buddies weren't trying to impress the others by their holiness. The three prayed that, whether folks frequented the bars for company or numbing, they might come to depend on the true "Spirit" that could bring them life instead of dependency. They also prayed for their family members who sat home alone and sometimes hoped to be in bed before their inebriated spouse or parent returned.

ಐಐ ಅಅ

Lillian decided to get to know the country club set. She and Walt had been invited to join, but time and money put membership out of reach. So, Lillian called a longtime member of the club and said she would like to become more familiar with what the club offered women, and would she take her along as a guest for a few times. Lillian met a number of women she knew, a few from her own church. She played bridge and golf and listened. In many ways the women she met were not all that unlike Lillian. They had families or were divorced. Most moms with young children felt like they were going crazy trying to cope with kids' growing up—all the more reason to take advantage of all the opportunities that affluence afforded.

Lillian noticed a significant difference in most of the women she met, however. They didn't have any Sure Foundation to their lives. Happy when things were going well, they were just as devastated when a job was lost, a relationship was broken, or health slipped away by a heart-breaking diagnosis. Life, for so many, felt like a broken teeter-totter bouncing them up or down without notice. Some claimed to be Christians, but for most, the "club" provided their community needs, and travel or recreation filled most Sundays. A level of love and acceptance seemed always available at the club, as long as the social code remained upheld, and their money didn't run out. Of course, most didn't even pretend confidentiality, and in fact, the gossip line was often wielded as a weapon against anyone who lost favor.

Lillian realized how easily she could have been sucked into the pride of the elite and how good she could have been at wearing plastic smiles. Her heart broke for the women who really believed that clothes and status could make them happy. While she held nothing against wealth, she knew full well how hard it is to serve God and one's entitled standard of living at the same time.

Lillian also spent time visiting with the other soccer moms at Evan's practice. She listened and asked questions. She learned that most of them were as harried as she had been. Some went to church, but few were able to challenge the Sunday game schedules, particularly league games away from home. Often the soccer community became their "church," the place where they met friends who also worshiped success in their kids, in hope of a sports scholarship. However, most of the mom friendships vanished as soon as the games or after-game parties were over. While a few of the soccer moms had good friends, the vast majority longed for someone to talk to, someone who would listen and be there for them.

The moms that didn't claim any kind of faith tended to see the church as a judgmental group of bigots who criticized others and thought themselves better. Many of the women admitted that they wouldn't mind trying church, but their husbands weren't up for it at all. The men held the same stereotypes as their wives about churchgoers and had plenty of other things to do with their time. Lillian was struck by the fact that neither the country-club set nor the soccer-moms saw any value in the church. Expressing many of their attitudes, one woman quipped, "Who knows if all that heaven crap is real anyway." Lillian knew that the false securities of this world would topple on the heads of the "self-made" women sooner or later. She wondered how many knew that real help, love, and stability are available to them in Jesus, and if they knew whom to ask if they wondered.

৪০৪০ ৫৫

Jim decided to visit the down-and-out crowd, the ones that knew they were down-and-out. He attended the local AA meeting, served food at the Rescue Mission, and volunteered as a stand-in Chaplain at the county jail. These places weren't new to Jim, but he had never really gone as a listener. In each place he let small talk evolve into more meaningful sharing. He was surprised by the large number in this group that had come to a radical faith in Jesus. Each one had his or her own story of personal loss, relational destruction, and sometimes near-death experiences. The ones that knew Jesus understood from experience that they needed a Savior and Lord. The ones that didn't know had reasons why "God" couldn't be trusted or, more often, why Christians couldn't be trusted. They told stories of being judged or let down by some church-going friend or relative. Some of their perceived rejections probably resulted from their own doing, but no doubt there had been many "Good Samaritans" who had failed them. When their lives tumble into trouble, most churches have little to offer. Jim sure knew that Emmaus Church stood ill-equipped to care for addicted or deeply hurting people. "Somehow we have to train church members to help people with addictions and mental illness," Jim thought. "Jesus, help us. How do we even get our people to care?"

ಏಏ ಬಬ

The next Thursday the three of them met at the church office to discuss their interviews. Barry and Lillian were also eager to hear what Jim had to say about the lesson Jesus had taught him. A comment by Lillian pretty well summed up what they had learned, so far. "Jesus is right. The world around us is filled with people who desperately need Him, people He loves. Meanwhile, we've designed church for ourselves, and, of course, anyone who insists on joining us."

They went on to discuss how uncomfortable they felt around people unlike themselves, how inadequately prepared they felt to help hurting people, and yes, how selfishly they had reacted when the needs of others threatened to interrupt their busy lives.

Barry reflected, "Jim, it isn't that you haven't challenged us to love our neighbors, it's just that guilt isn't strong enough to make us overcome our barriers to doing it. It took Jesus to do that, at least to inspire us to want to overcome them."

Jim responded, "Barry, you're right. We don't have what it takes to be God's messengers in the world, to love our neighbors. We need to live in our adoption and experience transformation. That's what Jesus told me to share with you. In fact, He told me that teaching people to understand the adoption and transformation process and how to live it represents most of my job."

Jim went on to share his conversation with Jesus about the Lord's plan to bring people into the abundant life of the Kingdom of God. He explained that God didn't just meddle in

144

the affairs of people, answering prayers here and denying them there. "Jesus told me that it's the way most people see Him—a capricious supreme power who needs to be convinced to do what people want Him to do. But, Jesus has a far greater plan. We're called to partner with Him in the exercise of His will and power in our world. He wants everyone to experience adoption as the Father's children—heirs who experience His love, who will help run the family business, so to speak, working with Him to bring His love and power to the world."

Barry interrupted, "Trouble is, people don't know they need adopting. Most think they're fine right where they are."

Lillian objected, "I'm not so sure. Maybe they just don't see a family worth being adopted into. It's one thing for some poverty-stricken, third-world kid to want to come to America, but for folks here, we Christians look just like everyone else. We don't demonstrate the real nature of the Kingdom of God. We don't show others the amazing forgiveness, love, power, and healing that exists here."

Jim replied, "Maybe we haven't realized what the Kingdom of God is supposed to be like either—until Jesus got in our face." He cleared his throat and said, "Okay, now let me continue. Jesus explained that people become adopted when they receive the forgiveness and love of God through faith in Jesus and His atoning death on the cross. You're right; communicating this offer of adoption proves time-consuming and frustrating. People have to see the reality of the Kingdom's abundant life, recognize the deadness of their lives without it, and realize that it's offered as a free gift. But then the hard part comes; they need to want abundant life enough to muster the courage to surrender to Jesus and His Lordship, to trust Him. Yet, the Holy Spirit helps those who truly want abundant life."

Jim shared the passage that Jesus had asked him to read out loud, asking Barry to read it this time. Barry opened his Bible, found the place in John 1, verse 12, and started, "But as many as received Him, to them He gave the right to become children of God, even to those who believe in His name, who

145

were born, not of blood nor of the will of the flesh nor of the will of man, but of God."

When Barry finished reading, Jim went on, "But adoption isn't just a matter of accepting Christ and joining a church; it's much more than that. Jesus used the example of an adopted kid and how hard it is to adjust to a new culture. Remember the Goodwins over on 5th Avenue who adopted that little girl from India? They had a terrible time before she learned the language and all the new customs. They struggled to get her to quit stealing; she'd done it all her life. She had to unlearn the survival habits that kept her from any real relationships. The same dependencies on the world lie within us, too. We know how hard it is to learn to know and love a God we can't see or hear, not to mention learning to live by the Ten Commandments rather than the 'anything-goes' lifestyle of the world. It's even harder to trust Jesus completely rather than depending on our possessions that're supposed to bring us happiness."

The group reflected silently for a few minutes. How well they remembered thinking that adoption, in the sense that Jim had used it in previous sermons, consisted mostly of joining a church. Now they realized that adoption meant accepting a whole new reality, a universe of love, more unseen than seen.

Lillian commented, "When you stop and think about it, we have to learn to look at life in a totally different way. It takes a lot of personal change to be able to live in God's Kingdom."

"You're right on target, Lillian. Jesus calls this change you mentioned, 'transformation.' To live fully in the adoption we're given, we need much more than a little behavior modification, we have to be transformed." Jim paused to let the thought sink in, then continued. "Okay, Lillian, it is your turn. Please read Romans 12:1 and 2."

Lillian took the Bible from Barry and read, "Therefore I urge you, brethren, by the mercies of God, to present your bodies a living and holy sacrifice, acceptable to God, which is your spiritual service of worship. And do not be conformed to this world, but be transformed by the renewing of your mind, so that you may prove what the will of God is, that which is good and acceptable and perfect."

Jim expounded, "The Holy Spirit transforms us. He gradually removes our hearts of stone and replaces them with the hearts of flesh that we were created to have, ones that can actually know and love God. That's what's been happening to each of us as we've talked to Jesus over these last few months. As we've longed to understand Him and become like Him, the Holy Spirit has been transforming us so that we can do just that. He has been growing the fruit of the Spirit in us. You know: love, joy, peace, patience, kindness, goodness, faithfulness, gentleness, and self-control. They're listed in Gal 5:22-23."

"Now hold on," Barry interrupted. "I thought it was just a matter of learning to act that way."

Lillian cut in, "Is that the way you experienced it, Barry? You just read it in the Bible, practiced real hard, and it all happened? As I remember your story, it wasn't that easy. It hasn't been for me, either."

Jim smiled, raising his eyebrows signaling his own assent. "That's exactly right. Knowing that we are loved unconditionally as God's children brings us a lot of peace and may free us to act a bit differently. However, our thinking's not the only problem. Our motivations need to be transformed as well. Selfishness and sin have made us unable to respond to God's love or to hear His voice. We need new hearts and new ears. It takes transformation from the inside out." Jim paused to get his breath.

"This transformation requires the surgery of the Holy Spirit. When we honestly desire one of the deeds of the flesh to be gone, I mean *really* want it gone, the Holy Spirit cuts it out of us and replaces it with the opposite trait. Love is His scalpel. Our hearts were designed by God to recognize authentic Love, the love only God can give. As in physical surgery, we still need the long process of recovery. Old habits die hard. We have to really want to use our new gift, just like you had to use your new knee to recover from your knee replacement, Barry. It took time and persistence, but it's His love that heals us. In time, we become more and more like Jesus."

Barry frowned again and replied, "The key to transformation lies in a person's willingness to really want to let go of the old way. The Holy Spirit won't just rip it out. We have to let go of it so we can take Jesus' hand instead." Barry chuckled, "We're like the monkeys that were caught in Africa. Poachers put a banana in a small mouth bottle hooked to a rope. The monkeys reached in to grab the banana, but couldn't get their hands out unless they let go of the banana, which they were unwilling to do. So, they became trapped. We get just as trapped by trying to hold on to the things that we depend upon instead of Jesus. When we take Jesus' hand in some issue, we simultaneously let go of what we were holding onto that enslaved us. For example, I had to let go of alcohol as a crutch before I could receive God's comfort. But I couldn't let go or receive with my own strength; the Holy Spirit helped me when I became desperate. Not only did He enable me to let go, but He showed me that I needed to do it in the first place."

"Exactly," replied Jim. "But many people get confused, thinking they're fine because they've become religious. Religion, comfortable Christianity, can counterfeit real conversion and real transformation, making us feel holy when we're still hanging on to all the old stuff. It's transformation that makes us able to become conformed to the image of Christ and to show others what the Kingdom of God is really like. They have to see it in us." Jim looked down and then went on quietly, "For my part, I've still got a lot of transformation to experience. Jesus said it takes a lifetime and we still never become perfect until heaven." The others nodded in agreement.

Barry sighed, "Wow. That's quite a lesson. How come you never told us that in church before?"

Lillian came to Jim's defense, "He's preached on those passages a hundred times, but I guess we weren't desperate enough to hear the real message."

Jim cut in, "That's kind of you, Lillian, but I'm not sure I had really grasped the full meaning of it or experienced much of it myself. Even now, I'm in the process of discovery. So I didn't do a very good job of making it clear to others. That makes my point: you can't take others where you haven't been yourself, or show them what you haven't seen." Jim shook his head sadly, and Barry and Lillian shifted in their seats as though the air in the room was becoming close. Barry looked at his watch.

"Don't get ready to go," Jim continued. "There's more, much more." Jim went on to share the passage from Ephesians 6:10-18 about the spiritual battle in which we're all engaged. He shared Jesus' analogy about the serf who had been adopted into the kings' household and made his son. Jim told them about the gift of the magic sword and the multiple battles, each of which the son lost until he learned to wield the sword, become a working part of the king's guard, and finally to hear and follow the King's instructions.

"It's that way with us," Jim continued. "We're in a war with the evil of this world that's trying to enslave God's loved ones. The Holy Spirit's transformation includes enabling us to live in the full armor of God, and teaching us how to wield the Sword of the Spirit with the gifts of the Spirit."

Jim's expression turned grave. He went on, "I'd never really understood the full impact of transformation before Jesus explained it. Even now it all still seems fuzzy. Yes, Jesus has overcome the world, but, as He explained it to me, He has entrusted the battle for the souls of others to us, His kids. As Jesus spoke, I'd never seen Him so serious. He told me that we, His followers, write the history of Emmaus and the world. Unless we're transformed into the kind of people who can wield the sword with God's love, all those people we visited this last week could be lost."

Silence filled the office as the ramifications of what Jesus had taught Jim seemed to press down upon them. Barry wondered if Elaine might still be alive if the church had really known how to pray. Lillian worried for her family. What might happen if they only experienced religion? Jim thought about the church and wondered if he had what it takes to pastor a sword-wielding congregation.

Lillian broke the silence, "I think I understand the concept, but it still sounds like it puts too much in our hands. Isn't Jesus the One that was sent to save the world? It's not up to us, is it?

That brings me to the next point, Lillian. "There's one other thing that Jesus said to share. Remember? He said He would lead us personally; He is the Shepherd, the leader of the church. We don't have to do it by ourselves. I think that's what He wants to talk to us about next Thursday—how we follow Jesus as Shepherd."

After a long pause, Lillian almost whispered, "What scares me is that I wonder how many people really want to follow Jesus as Shepherd."

The group closed their meeting with prayer that the Holy Spirit would empower them to hear their Shepherd's voice and follow Him faithfully.

ꙮꙮ ꙮꙮ

The trio continued their efforts to become more acquainted with the people of Emmaus. Having informally interviewed the rich and the poor and the down-and-out, they'd covered the categories that Jesus had asked. Each one, however, decided to keep visiting neighbors and friends, almost anyone who would talk with them.

One interesting insight came from people who attended other churches in Emmaus. Most of the faithful church members they met surprisingly held basically the same likes and dislikes that they'd earlier expressed about Emmaus Community Church. Similar to their own lists about Emmaus, the pros and cons seemed to have little to do with experiencing the presence of Jesus or caring for the needy of the community. Most of the folks they interviewed believed that church, simply an organization of its members, rather than the Body of Christ, existed for the members' comfort. Like Emmaus Church, these members of other churches felt happy enough when someone new visited or moved to town and joined—the new members helped pay the bills after all. But the bottom line for most focused on feeling better when they came out of church.

Barry and Lillian ran into several who complained about being bored with church, wishing for more—more meaning and more relevance. A few even wanted to experience God. But most had developed their religious habits and opinions years ago, well entrenched in the status quo. The three realized that an ingrown focus and the practice of virtually ignoring Jesus were not limited to Emmaus Community Church; the "it's-about-me" syndrome appeared epidemic. No wonder Jesus looked distressed as He shared His frustrations.

It started Tuesday evening. In two more nights they would meet again with Jesus, and the threesome wasn't fully looking forward to the meeting. When their visits with Jesus, particularly the private ones, focused on themselves, they anticipated each visit with great expectation. But now that the discussion had turned to the church and their roles in it, they awaited the meeting with much less enthusiasm.

What they later described as "dark thoughts" started for each of them around 9:00 P.M. Their shift in thinking followed pretty much the same line. Maybe these visits with Jesus weren't so great after all. Was He asking too much of any ordinary local church? Was He asking too much of them? After all, Emmaus was a nothing town and Emmaus Community Church had no real significance. Even if the whole town fell in love with Jesus, what difference would it make? A revival there wouldn't even rate a small mention in *Christianity Today.*

Barry began to think about his life before Jesus "arrived." "Sure I was unhappy, but I'd gotten used to it." He fondly recalled the previous predictability of his life. No, he didn't like drifting away from his boys and their families, but it had become "normal." They could handle it. Barry had felt comfortable blaming others for all his troubles, which he said, "Weren't all that bad." Now Jesus not only asked him to take responsibility for his own issues, but for those of the whole town, even the whole world. The phrase, "It's not fair," kept ringing in his ears. He didn't ask to become some Bible-swinging knight in God's Kingdom. He was just an ordinary farmer. Why had Jesus picked on him?

Similarly, Lillian became pensive and troubled. Life before Jesus' appearances had been too busy and stressful, but she battled no real crises. Maybe if she hadn't made the mistake of signing up for the Elder Board, Jesus wouldn't have chosen her. What seemed like a relatively simple life now took on much greater proportions than she ever dreamed. In the midst of this dark fog, she thought, "I know these people need Jesus, but I'm not a pastor. If the pastors in this town did their jobs, people wouldn't be in such a mess." All this stuff about adoption and transformation scared Lillian. "That's for theologians and evangelists," she said out loud.

By 9:30 P.M, after self-talk similar to Barry's and Lillian's, Jim found himself in a state of near panic. Sure, Jim had wanted a vibrant growing church. But all this sounded like a lot more than he was prepared for. Yes, Jesus was talking about all Christians living as knights, but when it comes right down to it, it's the pastor's neck that's on the line. This next meeting with Jesus could really be devastating. Jesus would probably ask Jim to do things that he couldn't do, things that would get him in trouble, even if he could do them. His people only expected a reasonable sermon, some light fellowship, and enough in the offering plates to pay the bills. What would they expect of him once they really believed these new expectations that Jesus insisted upon?

"No wonder Jesus got Himself killed!" Jim thought.

By 9:45 P.M, all three were actively considering ditching the Thursday meeting. It would be just too risky, too much for simple people like them. If they just didn't show, then Jesus would know that they weren't up to what He was asking of them and He would leave them alone. Things could go back to the way they were. Each one independently considered telling someone about seeing Jesus, just so Jesus would wipe out their memories and it would all be over. Not one of them slept a wink that night. They just toyed with dark thoughts.

Barry, the first one up on Wednesday morning, poured his coffee and headed to the barn. "Work to be done," he grumbled. He started feeding the pigs and then slumped on the bale of hay. He felt listless and tired. The thought came to him again about staying home on Thursday night. After all, he didn't feel very well.

As the morning sun reached for a higher place in the sky, a patch of warm sunlight settled on the bale of hay next to Barry—right where Jesus usually sat during their conversations. "I sure do miss those talks," Barry said out loud. "Wonder what He'd do if I stood Him up?" Barry pictured the face of Jesus. He imagined His forehead raise a little, his lips straight, His eyes moist, hurt by Barry's betrayal. The sun patch gradually moved off the hay bale, as if Jesus had left for heaven. Barry felt more alone than he had ever felt in his life, even when Elaine died.

Just as Barry seemed to be sinking into a deep pit of despair, the Light that flooded the hay bale seemed to spark in his mind. He jumped up and shouted, "No, You can't go; I don't mean the things I've been thinking. Damn! I am so sorry. Please forgive me. I'll see this through. But You've got to help me!" Barry sat and stared at the hay bale in silence and dismay.

Suddenly a terrifying thought came to him. He rushed into the house and grabbed the phone. He called Pastor Jim and

Lillian, "You gotta come over here right away!" As it turned out, Jim's meeting had cancelled and Lillian's kids were playing at a neighbor's house, so they both could come. "I'll be waiting in the barn," he told them. His voice sounded urgent and troubled.

When they arrived, they went directly to the barn. Barry sat on a bale of hay and motioned for them to join him on another. He told them about his fears and the thoughts he'd been nursing about standing Jesus up on Thursday night. "I am so ashamed," Barry confessed. Then he looked up at Jim and Lillian and said softly, "After I told Jesus He would have to help me, it occurred to me that maybe I wasn't the only one struggling with these dark thoughts. Maybe you were struggling with them, too."

Lillian's and Jim's eyes widened. They looked at each other, and hung their heads. First Jim confessed and then Lillian. They were all amazed at how similar their line of thinking and feeling had been. Jim said, "I don't think I could have betrayed Him, but it was close. If you hadn't called, Barry...."

Lillian nodded as tears streamed down her cheeks. "After all He has done for me, how could I have possibly entertained those thoughts?"

"What time did it start?" Jim asked. "Almost exactly at 9:00 P.M, right after the news, for me."

Lillian responded, "It was about the same time for me, too, right after I got the kids in bed. I was so tired and the thoughts just began to roll through my head.

"Same for me, Barry added. Right after the news."

The three sat motionless, maybe recognizing for the first time the dark shadows that had attacked them.

Jim continued, "It's almost like someone was playing the same message inside each of our heads. We may be the only people that Jesus has appeared to since biblical times, yet each of us considered betraying Him and the huge investment He's made in us. I would have never guessed I could entertain such

154

thoughts. How could I ever have lived with myself if I'd gone through with it?"

Silence hung over the barn like a funeral reception where no one knows what to say. Finally Jim spoke again, "You know, I don't think what happened to us was a coincidence. I think we were under direct attack from Satan. Remember the second line of that passage from Ephesians 6 about the Sword of the Spirit?" He repeated it from memory, 'For our struggle is not against flesh and blood, but against the rulers, against the powers, against the world forces of this darkness, against the spiritual forces of wickedness in the heavenly places.'"

Lillian added, "Jesus told us He wanted to shepherd us. Remember the passage where Jesus tells His disciples that the thief comes to...."

Barry flushed and finished the verse angrily, "'The thief comes only to steal and kill and destroy; I came that they may have life, and have it abundantly.' It's John 10:10." He regained his composure and went on, "Well the 'thief' sure came close to stealing everything Jesus has done for us, killing our faith, and destroying our trust—Jesus would never ask us to do something that's impossible for us."

The threesome joined hands and Jim prayed, "Thank You Jesus that You've also struggled with temptation. We're so grateful that Barry had the strength to resist and the courage to call us. Thank You for helping us see this attack for what it is, and for the power to resist. We love You and we'll be there on Thursday." Jim and Lillian thanked Barry again for turning to Jesus in the midst of temptation. They weren't sure they could have done it.

ഇൻഈ ൲൲

As the day went on, the reality of what happened to them began to sink in. Lillian and Barry had never given the devil much thought, except maybe in jokes. Jim was more aware, but all three were struck by the subtle nature of this attack and how easily they were duped into believing that the lies originated in their own thoughts. The fears behind the temptations were real enough. But now they realized the serious and sinister nature of the battle and wondered how much of their previous dark thinking over the years had actually originated from the enemy. The stark reality that Jesus was not only calling them into a spiritual battle for other people, but to one being fought in their own heads—a war that had been depriving them of joy for many years.

Now they could hardly wait for the next meeting with Jesus on Thursday evening. They wanted to learn how to live fully as adopted children of God and to experience the transformation that would bring them to life as adult children of their Father and warriors of their Kingdom.

Chapter 11: Presence Unseen

Seven thirty Thursday evening finally arrived. All three had come to the church early and were waiting for Jesus when He walked through the door. This time He brought no scones, cookies, or tea, but just walked up to each of them and gave them a long, loving hug. He sat in His rocker, a chair that would have amazing significance for Emmaus Community Church in the years to come. He appeared calm and warm, but serious.

"It's been a rough few days, hasn't it? You've learned a lot, seen a lot, and experienced the true nature of the battle we're in. How are you feeling?"

Jim was the first to respond, "I feel like my eyes opened for the first time, to myself, to those around me, to the warfare we're in, and to You, Lord."

Barry picked it up there. "Now I understand the dark cloud over this town and its people, the same one that's been over me for years. I'm amazed that I couldn't see it before. I just chalked it off to human nature. I never realized the kind of 'help' our sinful natures receive."

Lillian added, "I can't believe how weak I am. After all I have been through with You, Lord, and still I almost betrayed You. I might have, if Barry hadn't called."

Jesus' look of concern and sorrow revealed that He shared their pain. He smiled warmly and explained, "I know what you experienced and went through the same terrible temptation. You have the additional problem, however, that your hearts and wills have been crippled by the presence of sin. Not all of what the devil said to you proved to be lies, right? He just twisted half-truths to divert your attention from me to yourselves and your fears, trying to get you to draw the wrong conclusions. But you had the benefit of knowing about my Presence and one another's support. It's no wonder that so many others don't fare so well." Jesus let the group reflect silently and then asked, "Where do you think our discussion should go from here?"

They needed no long pause to give them time to think. Each one knew where they needed to go, where they had to go. Jim responded for the group. "We want to learn to live as your adult children and follow You as your warriors of love. We want to discover how to live fully in our adoption and to experience the transformation that makes that life possible. We want our church to be a place that helps others do the same."

Jesus beamed, "I love you all so much. Together, we can do all of that. You'll have to let me teach you how, though." Jesus stood and stepped to each one with a warm embrace.

They all returned to their chairs and Jesus leaned forward and began, "I want to teach you so many things so that you can teach the church. First, however, you need to learn to experience my Presence just as fully when you can't see, hear, and touch me. I can't continue to meet with you this way forever; eventually it would stunt your growth."

"That's hard to believe," Lillian quipped. "You said that You would shepherd us. Even with the amazing meetings we've had, seeing You face to face, we are still weak. What will happen when You go away?"

"That's precisely the point, Lillian," Jesus responded. "Just because you can't see or touch or hear me directly doesn't mean that I'm gone or not leading you." The three raised their eyebrows with doubt, but Jesus continued, "Remember what I told my first disciples about my need to 'go away'? Barry, why don't you read about it in My Book? Turn to the beloved disciple's account, John, chapter 14, and start in the 25th verse."

Barry picked up "Jesus' Book" from the table, turned to the passage and began to read, "These things I have spoken to you while abiding with you. But the Helper, the Holy Spirit, whom the Father will send in my name, He will teach you all things, and bring to your remembrance all that I said to you. Peace I leave with you; my peace I give to you; not as the world gives do I give to you. Do not let your heart be troubled, nor let it be fearful."

"Do you understand what I'm saying there? The Holy Spirit connects us. The Holy Spirit lives in the communion and the power that the Father and I share. When He's with you, in you, We're right there as well. That's how I can be present everywhere, guiding all my brothers and sisters. In Him, I speak to you and am present to you. The Holy Spirit even helps you pray." Jesus rocked in His chair, waiting for His teaching to become clear to Jim, Lillian, and Barry.

"Lillian, it is your turn to read. My friend Paul experienced the Holy Spirit's help and shared what he learned with the church in Rome. Read the 8th chapter, starting with verse 26."

Lillian took the Bible from Barry, turned to the passage and read, "In the same way the Spirit also helps our weakness; for we do not know how to pray as we should, but the Spirit Himself intercedes for us with groanings too deep for words; and He who searches the hearts knows what the mind of the Spirit is, because He intercedes for the saints according to the will of God."

Jesus continued, "The Holy Spirit will help you learn to discern my Presence and even guide your conversations with me. I am present with you individually, and I'm particularly discernible when you're together." Your confidence that I am always present provides the essential key to living as my followers.

Jim spoke up, "I've known that truth as a doctrine for years, but we all know that it didn't make much of a difference in the way I followed or didn't follow You. What will make it different now? Is it because we have actually seen You? What about all the people who will never see You with their eyes until they get to heaven?"

"That's a very good question, Jim. People must first come to really believe it is possible to experience me as Present, and then they must actually let me make myself known to them. Knowing something means more than just believing it's true with your mind; you 'know' when you actually experience the reality." Jesus leaned back in His rocking chair and said, "Let's practice a bit."

The group looked surprised as Jesus' directed them to move the table out of the center and draw their chairs close to His rocking chair.

Once they settled in their chairs, Jesus began, "You're used to experiencing the world around you with your five senses. Most all living things have five senses. But because you are created in my image, you have a sensing heart as well. You must learn to use the spiritual senses of your heart, guided and empowered by my Spirit. Would you like to try it?" The three nodded cautiously.

"Well, let's begin. First, we'll deal with sight, as I take that away." Suddenly, Jesus disappeared. Yet, they could hear His voice. "You can't see me, but you can still hear me. Am I any less present with you? Do you feel that I've left in some way?"

Jim responded for the group, "No, Lord, we know You're here. We can hear You."

Jesus replied, still invisible, "Good. Now let's take away another sense and see how that works. I'll stop talking to your ears, but I'll speak to your heart." Just as Jesus said, no words emanated from the chair. The three sat and wondered what would happen next. Slowly the same thought occurred to each of them, "I want you to reach out and touch me." They all obeyed, and sure enough, they could feel Jesus' knees and arms. Lillian even got up and found His face and kissed Jesus on the cheek.

Jesus reappeared laughing out loud, and said, "How wonderful and I loved the kiss! Do you understand what happened? The Holy Spirit knew what I wanted and spoke it to you, silently as it were, in your hearts. Because you were attentive, you recognized my instruction." The group felt clearly delighted with the experiments. Jesus went on, "Now let's take away another sense: touch. I want you to experience this in two ways: first alone, and then by clasping hands. Don't try to listen with your ears or look with your eyes; they won't help. Just feel or sense with your heart."

The three sat back in their chairs and glanced down in thought. When they looked up, the rocker appeared empty. They sat for several minutes and tried to let their heart "feel." What did it mean to feel Jesus' presence with their hearts? Each one made imaginary attempts to raise some sort of inner antenna or radar or sonar dish, but nothing happened. Soon, they relaxed and just became still. In the stillness they experienced a peace, a safety, and yes, a Presence. It was the sense they had experienced in their meetings with Jesus. Soon, Barry put his hand on Lillian's who in turn touched Jim, who reached for Barry. Rather than try the antennas, they continued to sit in silence. Soon an emotional warmth and love filled them, as though they were holding Jesus' hands.

"He's still here," whispered Lillian.

The three almost jumped out of their chairs when suddenly Jesus' voice boomed, "That's great! You did wonderfully!" Jesus again appeared sitting in the rocking chair, grinning widely. "Isn't this fun?" Everyone chattered about their various and often unique experiences of sensing Jesus' Presence. Finally, Jesus interrupted, "We've yet to experiment with the most fundamental way to experience me. Remember the passage we read in John, chapter 14, verse 17? I taught about the Holy Spirit who 'abides with you and will be in you.' The Holy Spirit and I travel together." Jesus grinned. Here's what we'll do. I want you to become still, as you did before. This time, however, I would like you each to take turns sitting in my rocking chair for a few minutes."

Barry commented, "You mean sit on your lap?"

"That does sound kind of weird," Jim chimed in.

"Hey, guys," Lillian quipped, "I'll sit on Jesus' lap anytime.

Jesus smiled and waved toward His chair, "Just do it." He settled into His chair and bowed His head. "Holy Spirit, thank you for helping us experience the reality of Our Presence."

Lillian, Jim, and Barry followed Jesus' lead and bowed in prayer. When they glanced up, Jesus had disappeared. Lillian moved immediately and sat in the rocking chair for three minutes. Barry took his turn, followed by Jim.

Once they had returned to their original spots, Jesus reappeared. "Well, how did it go?"

This experiment felt harder to me than the other ones. I didn't know what to expect. Before, I could imagine touching You or hearing your voice of thoughts. But I've never experienced sharing the same physical space with another person. At first I imagined Your hands in mine and your eyes looking out through my eyes, which really didn't help. Finally, when I stopped trying to make something happen and just became still, I actually did sense you closer to me than sitting across from me in the room. It felt wonderful actually."

"Describe it," Jesus prompted.

Lillian cocked her head in reflection. "Well, I can say that I didn't have any physical sensations, nor did I sense thoughts from You. I would say that I felt very peaceful, safe, and profoundly together. The word *alone* could never have been used to describe me in that situation…if that makes sense."

Barry cleared his throat. "The first thought that came to my mind was snuggling with Elaine as we'd fall asleep. It felt like our hearts almost beat in sync. That thought made me really uncomfortable, you know, with You being a man and all,

Lord. Once I got over that, I just relaxed and imagined You and me sitting in the chair with our molecules interspersed. This time, it felt almost like a party, my cells enjoying Your cells. Then I noticed Your great faith added to my little faith. I could see that, with You in me, anything is possible. Any hint of fear absolutely disappeared." Glancing at Lillian, he concluded, "It was wonderful!"

Everyone looked at Jim, wondering what he might share. "I'm afraid that my experience in Your chair, in Your Presence, felt most 'wonderful.' First, I didn't sense You in *me*, rather I felt that I had moved into You. I looked at Barry and Lillian through Your eyes and could feel Your deep love for them. Then the scene changed and I could see what You saw when we talked out on Fox Hill. I looked with You over our town, into the homes and businesses, and I felt your pain, maybe even anguish, over the people who live without You. I saw all the potentials of abundant life you want for them and I could even sense the destiny of eternal death from which You long to rescue them. Rather than 'wonderful,' I would describe the experience as amazing and humbling."

"We work together just that way. You trust my Presence by faith. Then the Holy Spirit makes you aware of our connectedness. Sometimes you'll sense or feel or even receive my thoughts. But other times you may not feel or sense anything. It may well feel like I have in fact left you. But there are reasons for my seeming absence. First, your minds overflow with distractions, your own thoughts, tasks you want to do during the day, feelings about others, and so on. It's hard to remain really attentive. It may have felt easy this time because we started off the way we did and you're together. The Holy Spirit works very gently; He will not overpower you against your wills. He will wait. So, sometimes you don't discern me because you're distracted. But you can learn to become still and wait."

Jesus continued, "There's another reason you may not experience my Presence. People are so used to thinking of me 'up there' somewhere, in heaven. They expect to experience me externally, like you have in our face-to-face visits. But in adoption, We, the Trinity, come to live inside you." Jesus put His hand on His own heart and then swung it toward each of theirs. Then He continued, "Barry, you were reading John, chapter 14; now would you read the 16th through the 18th verses?"

Barry found the passage and read, "I will ask the Father, and He will give you another Helper, that He may be with you forever; that is the Spirit of truth, whom the world cannot receive, because it does not see Him or know Him, but you know Him because He abides with you and will be in you. I will not leave you as orphans; I will come to you."

"Thanks, Barry. Now let's add to that. Jim, read my friend Paul again. Look up Colossians, chapter 1, and read verses 25 through 27."

Jim turned and read, "Of this church I was made a minister according to the stewardship from God bestowed on me for your benefit, so that I might fully carry out the preaching of the word of God, that is, the mystery which has been hidden from the past ages and generations, but has now been manifested to His saints, to whom God willed to make known what is the riches of the glory of this mystery among the Gentiles, which is Christ in you, the hope of glory."

Jesus summed up. "What we've just heard stands as bedrock in our relationships. I'm not only present WITH you, I'm present IN you. What's more, you are present IN Us. The Kingdom of God exists where God rules. You live in the Kingdom because you believe in me; you've been adopted. You not only live 'in' the world, but you exist in the Kingdom of God; it's your new home. You live IN God, and We IN you. We're present with you more profoundly than any other relationship possible. But, as I was saying, my followers usually expect to sense my Presence 'outside' them, and so they miss me altogether. While I can appear to people externally, as I did with Saul on the road to Damascus and with John on the island of Patmos, our normal and ongoing relationship remains internal."

Jesus waited for his listeners to digest what He said and then continued, "Control provides another important reason my followers fail to experience my Presence. At the very core of human sinfulness lies the desire to control one's life and destiny, and even to control God. People often don't even notice what they're doing. For example, instead of opening their Bibles and waiting for me to reveal myself, or sitting silently just to be with me, they try to make me follow their lead. How many millions of times have I heard something like, 'Okay, Jesus, now I want You to teach me in this passage of the Bible.' What's implied however is 'And if You don't, I will think of something myself.' Or, there's the one that goes like this: 'Okay, Jesus, I'm very busy. I've managed to work You into my schedule for the next few minutes. Most of that time I will talk and You will listen. If there's time and You want to say something to me, You'd better get to it. Oops, sorry, I gotta run." The threesome laughed, but thought of the many times they'd done exactly that.

Jesus went on, "You see, I love you too much to let you get away with it, to reinforce that kind of behavior. It would be like giving a two-year-old candy anytime she asked for it. Two-year-olds think they run the world already. No, I have to make you wait, wait until you're tired of controlling, faced with the fact that it doesn't work. Most people have to become desperate to know my Presence to the point they're willing to surrender and let me lead them as their Shepherd. Even for believers, control is so ingrained that surrender has to be an ongoing process. Unfortunately, I often have to let people wait a very long time. It's not uncommon for people hold out until they're literally on their deathbeds and have lost everything before they can let themselves experience my Presence, their Shepherd and Lord."

Jim spoke up. "So, let me see if I understand. Even though we won't be able to see or hear You, we'll be able to experience Your Presence in some tangible way through a feeling or awareness. We just have to be careful not to let distractions get in the way or expect some external sensation, or try to take control of the relationship or time. You'll be with us through the Holy Spirit leading and guiding us. That sounds simple enough, but…."

Jesus interrupted and said, "Yes, Jim, it does sound simple and it is. The trouble is that it takes time and patience to learn how to cooperate with me in that way—in your head and in your heart. It's like telling a man with a broken hip that all he has to do is walk straight and be careful. No, the hip will take time to heal and the man will have to exercise and learn to walk in a different manner. It's the same for you. It may sound easy to simply 'walk with Jesus,' but people forget that they start off blind, lame, and without strength. It takes time to learn to let the Holy Spirit help them see spiritually, heal wounds that disable them, and empower them to respond. It takes some concentrated time and practice. In fact, the best way to learn to follow me begins in the prayer closet. You must make time to draw apart with me, learn to listen, and sense my Presence without all the external distractions. Once you have learned to listen and discern when you're in prayer, you will begin to discern me in the busyness of daily life."

Barry leaned forward with a question. "But what about the Bible? I thought the Scriptures contain Your word to us and that we're supposed to hear from You in your Word."

Jesus responded, "That's an excellent question, Barry, and I'm glad you asked it. The answer is very important for anyone who wants to live as my brother or sister and follow Me." Jesus turned to the group, "First, tell me what you know about the Bible."

Lillian spoke up, "The Bible is the inspired word of God, the authority for what we believe and contains the instructions for how we're supposed to live."

"Good," replied Jesus. "Anything else?"

Barry chimed in, "The Bible contains a collection of documents written by various authors such as Moses, David, the Prophets, and the Apostles who tell the stories of God's people and His interaction with them. The New Testament was written by Your Apostles and their companions at the direction of the Holy Spirit so that we could believe in You."

"Great," Jesus responded.

Jim added his perspective, "All that's true, but we have to understand the Bible in the context in which it was written. For example, the people of the Old Testament were under the law of the Ten Commandments and other rules that God set up. When You came, You fulfilled the Law and reestablished our relationship with God through Your cross. You offered us forgiveness and eternal life as a gift of grace that we could receive through faith. So, we have to be careful about imposing the Old Testament rules of law on us New Testament Christians. But the Ten Commandments, while their violation won't keep Christians out of heaven, remain as a standard of God's will for us. Cultural customs which may have applied then may not apply now, too." Jim paused and then went on, "The trouble is that lots of folks don't agree about how to interpret those things. Some churches come up with a lot of 'out-of-date' rules and perspectives; some other churches let anything go. We certainly need the Bible, and we need You, the Word of God, to help us understand it and apply it."

"Very good," Jesus grinned. "You've been doing your homework." He paused and went on. "The Bible records God's interaction with people over time. The Holy Spirit guided its writing from Genesis through Revelation. He guided the leaders who collected and kept these books so that the next generations might learn from what their ancestors experienced. The authors recorded this history in various forms such as literal accounts, prophecies, songs, allegories, poetry, collected sayings, letters, and mystical revelations. The Holy Spirit not only inspired these writings and their collection, He also inspires their reading by people who have the Holy Spirit in them."

Jesus continued, "The Bible, My Book," He said smiling, "represents the operating instructions from the Manufacturer. It describes who God is, what He's like, and how to live at peace with Him. Because God's wisdom spans farther than any created being's capability to grasp, many passages can be hard to comprehend unless the Holy Spirit sheds light upon them. For example, people have a hard time understanding how God can be perfectly just and perfectly compassionate at the same time. They struggle to grasp how God can be Love itself and yet punish rebellion. How can a God of love have perfect power and let millions suffer with war, injustice, and starvation? People tend to think that if they just study the Bible enough, with biblical experts of their liking to explain it, all God's mystery will be solved. The world will never exhaust the mystery of God, even with the Bible."

Jesus went on, "Having said that, the children of God throughout the ages have studied the Bible with the inspiration of the Holy Spirit. Through instruction by learned elders they come to know the truth about God, about themselves, and about God's Kingdom. They learned what it meant to live like a child of God through adoption and transformation. The great mysteries of God's ultimate plan for humanity were revealed, and they glimpsed the eternal life that would be given to them in this life and in the new heaven and earth. They discovered through my teachings, as well as the examples and teachings of my followers, how to become children of God and live as my followers. So, reading and understanding the Bible remains essential."

A concerned expression came over Jesus' face and He continued, "But there's also a danger related to honoring the Bible. You could compare the danger to treading on a narrow road with steep slopes on either side. Some try to completely limit their experience of the Creator of the Universe to the written words of the Bible. God can never be contained in a book, no matter how holy or inspired it is. You were created to have fellowship with God, not just a book about Him. Some people even end up in a form of idolatry—they worship the book about God, My Book, rather than God Himself. The Bible remains important, even vital for my children, but it was never intended as a substitute for me personally. People have made that mistake in various ways throughout history." Jesus paused as if remembering millions of His would-be followers who never really came to know Him.

"On the other side of the narrow road, some find the Bible too hard to understand or don't agree with some of its values and requirements, so they dismiss it altogether. This dismissal of the Bible often starts with one particular teaching that the person or group doesn't like. For example, many people resent that I have designed sexuality as an expression of the love between a man and a woman, as a gift of the pleasure of participating with me in creation. So, they dismiss those teachings and replace them with what they think seems more reasonable. Others stumble over the story of Creation and get distracted by the time it took. So, they dismiss the creation story. And so it goes, until some of my followers find themselves left without any authority but their own. They deny the clear teaching of God and reap the disaster that comes with ignoring the operating instructions of the Manufacturer."

Barry squirmed, looking like he'd gotten more than he bargained for. But Jesus pushed on, "But for those who know me and desire to know me better, the Bible stands as a powerful tool in the hands of the Holy Spirit. As my followers read with a humble and attentive heart, listening for my voice, the Holy Spirit impresses particular words, phrases, or stories upon them, passages particularly relevant to their needs at the time. How many times have you read Scripture and been instructed, cautioned, or encouraged? But, again, it's not the book that speaks, but My Spirit who speaks through it to the hearts that listen and wait." Jesus paused and then turned to Barry, "Thanks, Barry, for introducing the importance of the Bible to

169

the process of experiencing my Presence. It may feel like we got sidetracked a bit, but understanding how to use the Bible remains critical."

Jesus looked at His watch and exclaimed, "Well, this is enough for tonight. I've given you a lot to chew on, truths critical to your ability to walk with me as my beloved, and to minister with Me in My Kingdom."

Jesus rose abruptly from His chair, headed toward the door and then paused. "I have another assignment for you this week. Between now and the time we meet next Thursday, I want you to practice becoming attentive to my Presence. You'll need to plan for a specific time each day to work at it, a place with as few distractions as possible. Once you're settled, say what you need to tell me, but keep it simple; I already know. Then just become still and attentive, just as you did in our practice session a few minutes ago." Jesus grinned and went on, "During the rest of the day and at church on Sunday, watch for me. Listen and see with your hearts what I'm trying to say and do in you and around you. Become intentional about following my shepherding. We'll talk about your experiences next week and then continue our discussion about the Holy Spirit and how He works to make you warriors for my Father and lovers of souls."

Chapter 12: Warriors of the Kingdom

Thursday nights had become sacred for Barry, Lillian and Jim. Now, nothing could keep them away, even sickness, which interestingly never occurred. Each week became measured from Thursday to Thursday, with Sunday a midpoint opportunity to listen, observe, and relate daily experiences to the lessons Jesus had taught. They each had to admit that "church" began to feel quite different. Instead of going for the part that interested them, such as the sermon or the music or their friends, they now watched for Jesus in every aspect, letting the Holy Spirit point out discoveries to be explored.

For example, all three noticed that several of the people they visited in the community started coming to church. The three had been quite careful not to talk about the church, even when questioned, and not to suggest that their interviewees come. Yet, here they were, checking it out, listening for what their hearts craved. Lillian and Barry became particularly attentive to people standing alone before and after church, and made friendly contacts. These people came looking for Jesus, but all the activity could obscure His Presence. A face-to-face greeting from someone who genuinely wanted to get to know them, however, often communicated more than all the words of the church service.

For some months, Emmaus Community had been using the Church Calendar lectionary to select the Scripture

171

texts to be read on Sunday. Pastor Jim often preached about one of the Old Testament, Epistle, or Gospel texts, listening for the Spirit's guidance about what Jesus wanted to say to the people. The lectionary helped Jim preach beyond his pet subjects to the whole of the Gospel message. Barry, Lillian, and Jim were struck by the amazing "coincidences" between one or more of the texts and their discussions with Jesus, or an issue that had been simmering in their lives. Eventually they came to expect these connections, listening closely to each reading. No longer did the texts appear merely as an introduction to the theme of the day and the sermon; now the passages became vital proclamations about their life with God. Before experiencing the Presence of Jesus, they would never have accepted that Scripture passages, chosen decades or centuries ago for a given Sunday, could speak to them so directly.

Barry and Lillian noticed a dramatic change in the new depth of Pastor Jim's preaching. First, they sensed a new depth of humility in him. Now he often illustrated his points with stories of his own struggles or failures. They also observed that he no longer focused on merely conveying information or attempting to get people to adopt some new behavior. No, Jim spoke about Jesus—messages from Jesus—calling his hearers to a deeper and more personal relationship with Him. Jim addressed not only their minds, but their hearts. His sermons flew like arrows of wisdom aimed right where each person yearned for hope and truth and love. Barry and Lillian often wept inwardly as they listened, understanding the deep love of Jesus that shone in their pastor's countenance during the service.

Not only did his sermons change, but his prayers radiated new life. He often used the Lord's Prayer in creative ways, asking the congregation to pray it responsively with him, or to stand silently, pondering each petition. The people might say a line or phrase, and then Jim would pray its meaning related to the hearts and lives of the congregation, community, and world. Prayer changed from an often rote part of the liturgy to a profoundly moving experience. Each person felt prayed for and blessed personally, sensing that the prayers somehow contained power that began to accomplish what they spoke. Many other signs of life started emerging that would more fully materialize much later, but Jim, Lillian, and Barry already spotted Jesus in hundreds of ways every Sunday. Sometimes, key words of Scripture seemed to carry a unique weight as if to say, "listen." Unexpectedly, tears revealed emotions within them that had been stirred by the Lord. Conversations with people at church sometimes seemed to carry an important message. Conversely, they became conscious of Jesus' desire to speak through them to others. As another person shared, a response often came to mind that carried a particular loving intensity. They noticed that when they tenderly shared these thoughts, others were particularly encouraged or helped. They returned home after church, blessed to have been witnesses to the great love of God. Meanwhile, they continued their attempts to connect intentionally with the invisible, yet Present, Jesus each day.

৪৩৪৩ ৫৪৫৪

The next Thursday meeting finally came. Barry, Lillian, and Jim arrived with great enthusiasm, ready to share what they'd been experiencing. They felt exhilarated, like the seventy disciples who returned to Jesus with the stories of the demons who'd been cast out.

As Jesus walked into the room, they stood up with surprise and confusion. Jesus came dressed in first century attire, much like they'd seen in statues or paintings. He also wore a simple crown of gold, like the one Jim had seen in his first encounter and invitation. Jesus smiled and explained, "Like my threads? I've been dressing in a manner that would make you feel more comfortable. But you know, in my whole time on earth I dressed like this, minus the crown of course—I rather like it—not so tight and less constraining, I guess."

The three just stood and stared until Jesus motioned for them to sit. He took the rocking chair and continued, "I have dressed to make myself feel familiar to you. I'm your friend, your brother, your beloved, your fellow child of our Heavenly Father. Yet I'm also your King. I've been entrusted by my Father with your leadership and your salvation, and with your very lives. It's my Father's will that I see you safely through the journey."

Lillian started to interrupt with her questions, "What journey; where are we going?"

But Jesus steadfastly continued, "We've become better friends than you ever guessed possible. You are my beloved! But you must also remember that you are the beloved of the King of Kings, the Lord of Lords, Your Master. While I love each of you dearly, I must also rule you and lead you. Although I'm your friend, you must obey me in every aspect of life if you're to realize all that I have for you and celebrate God's victory with me in heaven. Will you follow me as your King?"

Jesus' regal look and pleading tone melted their hearts and tears streamed down their cheeks. Jesus stood, motioning for them to rise. Laying His hands upon their heads in blessing, Jesus said softly, "Here, one day, your own crown will rest. Prepare yourselves well to wear it."

It took several minutes for the three to recompose themselves and return to their seats. Finally Jesus said, "There's more I must teach you tonight, more about the Holy Spirit and the help He offers you. But first, tell me about discovering My Presence during this last week."

Jim responded first. "So much has changed I hardly know where to start. My new position as 'under-shepherd' has proved to be a lot of fun. Sermon preparation has been transformed from a burden into a fascinating discovery of what You want me to share with the people. I've actually started worshiping in church on Sunday mornings. Normally it's the last place I could really worship."

Barry chimed in, looking at Jim, "Your sermons have become wonderful, Jim! There's a new tone of humility and love to them." Turning to face Jesus, he added, "I feel You, Jesus, speaking to me through Jim each time."

"And the prayers!" Lillian put her hand on Jim's shoulder. "They're beautiful! You pray to our Lord present in the room rather than to someone up in the sky. Your prayers fill us with confidence and faith and they lift us up in expectancy."

"Now let me finish," Jim cut in with some embarrassment. "There's a difficult side to this, too. I have to confess that my intentional times alone with You and have been harder. I'm still not sure I've found the right time or place to be alone with You. In the early mornings I need to help Kate with Brian. Then I often schedule breakfast meetings with men in the church or with other pastors. Once my day gets rolling, I become so driven by my schedule that it's hard to stop until it's time to go home. Maybe I should schedule 3:30 in the afternoon in my office each day, like You and I used to do. Even when I've found a quiet place to be with You, my mind bounces all over the map. It's so hard to concentrate. I have a lot to learn about being attentive both in prayer and in my daily activities." Jim sighed. "Wouldn't it be a lot easier if You just sent me an email entitled, 'Dear Stupid,' and told me what to do?"

Everyone laughed, but Jesus looked at Jim with a twinkle and asked, "Would you really be happy with an email relationship? Are instructions for the day all you need from me?"

Jim flushed. "Of course not, Lord. I need to experience Your love. I need to let the Holy Spirit transform me. It's really hard, but I'll keep at this prayer thing until it becomes natural."

"And I'll help you!" Jesus offered with a smile.

Lillian shared some of her same frustrations about finding a time where she could be alone with God. Then when she did, she worried about not praying correctly. "I get all messed up with the process. Should I start the time with a Bible verse like I used to do in my quiet times? How much should I talk and how much should I listen? What should I expect to happen? I get so frustrated with myself."

Jesus smiled lovingly, "The important thing, Lil, is that you're taking the time at all and most of all doing it because You love me." He paused and then turned to Barry. "Barry, how about you?"

"For me, time and place aren't a problem. I'm alone in the barn or the field, and live alone; no one's going to bother me. But, I also struggle about what should happen during the time I've set aside? I can't just sit there. I feel like I have to do something, like read a Bible passage or a devotional book. Then I remember that I'm there to be with You, Lord. So I try to spend most of the time being still. Then, like Jim and Lillian, my mind bounces all over the place, as if it's looking for something to keep me from listening to You. Focusing on You works a lot better when we were all together, like this."

Jesus' response to their frustrations surprised them all. "Isn't that wonderful?" He exclaimed. "You're all making real progress. As I told you before, it takes time to learn to become attentive to Someone you can't see or feel or hear. It's your job to find the time and place and to honor it. But remember the Holy Spirit will connect us together. Just be as still as you can and let Him do His work. Also, remember that I never break my promises. When I say that I will never leave you or forsake you, I mean it. I'm with you, whether you feel me or not. My Spirit communes with your spirit whether or not you have any insights or experiences. Stand on your faith, not on what you think should be some successful outcome." Jesus paused and then went on. "You'll learn, I promise. And as you do, prayer times will become the most precious parts of your life and a wonderful joy to me."

Jesus adjusted His rocker in the circle, His demeanor becoming more focused and intentional. "Now I'd like to change the direction of our conversation back to the power of the Holy Spirit in you and in the church. Jim shared with you about adoption and transformation. He repeated my teaching about the full armor of God and told you the story about the serf who was adopted into the King's family, and how the boy had to learn to use his sword and to hear and obey the King. Now you understand that not only does the Holy Spirit connect you to me and you to one another, He also gives you power—heavenly power. It's the same Power that created the heavens and the earth, the same Power that raised me from the dead."

Jesus smiled and leaned forward in the rocker, "Following me can be exciting and really quite natural. I don't expect you to serve me and love others with your own power, but with mine. Let me ask you a question." Jesus paused and the three settled in their chairs attentively. "What makes people believe in me? Why should people believe that I rose from the dead, that I offer them eternal life, that there is a place for them in my Kingdom, and that abundant life is real? Why should anyone believe just because someone tells them that it's true?"

The three sat and thought for a few minutes. Then Lillian responded first. "Well, it is true," she protested. "Maybe because so many of us believe, others will too."

Barry took his turn. "We should try to love other people. Your Word says, 'You shall know them by their love.' If people see that we're different, then maybe they'll believe us."

Jim added his thoughts, "Isn't the Holy Spirit supposed to show people the truth of the Gospel when they hear it? We just have to get out there and tell people."

Jesus shook His head. "You're all partially right, but expressing some commonly held misconceptions. If you think about it, your reasoning doesn't hold water. People can deny or avoid many truths; the Holy Spirit doesn't force faith on people. Loving others is certainly the right thing to do, but many compassionate people live in the world. I designed love into people as a human characteristic that reflects God's nature, but many who don't follow me show love to others. You know the statistics. On the whole, the institution that calls itself by my name isn't seen as any more loving than the rest of the population. In fact, it's often seen as bigoted and judgmental, filled with people who look down on others. Finally, to respond to your point, Brother Jim, to whom was the Great Commission spoken? It was addressed to you, not to the Holy Spirit. I don't play mind games with people or hypnotize them into believing."

The three sat speechless. They obviously weren't getting what Jesus was after.

After another long pause, Jesus continued to help them think through the conundrum they faced. "Think about it. How did I get people to believe? How did you see the Apostles do it?" Jesus went on before anyone could answer. "We told people about the love of God and then we demonstrated that love through power. Sometimes people experienced that power through the love of the community. Sometimes they saw it in miracles that showed that God is real and that He loves them. These miracles acted as signs that pointed to a greater reality. Many people came to me because they needed something and had no other way to get it. Some came out of curiosity. The result? Hungry people found food. Lost people discovered hope. Lonely people received love and a family. They actually *experienced* the reality of adoption and transformation in the community of my followers; they weren't just told about it.

Once they experienced the truth of the Kingdom, they wanted it for themselves; they wanted to believe. When people want to believe, the Holy Spirit helps them."

Jesus motioned to Barry, "Would you read Ephesians, chapter 2, verses 8 and 9?" Barry opened the Bible, turned to the passage and read, "...for by grace you have been saved through faith; and that not of yourselves, it is the gift of God; not as a result of works, so that no one may boast." Barry closed the Bible and Jesus explained, "You see? The Holy Spirit helps you tell about my Presence, He helps you demonstrate it, and He helps those you're caring for to move from wanting to believing, from doubt to faith."

Jim objected. "But all that happened because You and Your special apostles accomplished those miracles. You can't expect that of us; we're just ordinary people." Lillian and Barry nodded agreement.

Jesus looked at Jim. "I thought you knew your Bible and your theology better than that, Jim. Yes, I am the Son of God, and I was there. But first of all, I had no more power than you do. Remember the Scriptures that explained that I 'emptied myself' when I became human? I gave up my prerogatives as God. I was just as dependent on the Holy Spirit as you are right now. Secondly, the Scriptures record, with blatant honesty the simple nature of my disciples, and how they struggled. They too had to depend on the Holy Spirit. So can you."

Jesus went on. "I want you to read a few familiar passages to help you remember what I'm talking about. Jim, start with First Corinthians, the 12th chapter, verses 4 through 11."

Jim took the Bible from the table, and feeling a bit scolded, he read: "Now there are varieties of gifts, but the same Spirit. And there are varieties of ministries, and the same Lord. There are varieties of effects, but the same God who works all things in all persons. But to each one is given the manifestation of the Spirit for the common good. For to one is given the word of wisdom through the Spirit, and to another the word of knowledge according to the same Spirit; to another faith by the same Spirit, and to another gifts of healing by the one Spirit, and to another the effecting of miracles, and to another prophecy, and to another the distinguishing of spirits, to another various kinds of tongues, and to another the interpretation of tongues. But one and the same Spirit works all these things, distributing to each one individually just as He wills."

Jesus went on, "I received those gifts from the Holy Spirit at my baptism; I gave them to my disciples; then they were made available to everyone at Pentecost and given to you when you believed and were baptized."

Jesus shook His head and continued, "Yet, a lot of people insist on modifying those passages, at least as they interpret them. Many of my followers look at wisdom, knowledge, and faith as mere human abilities. Then they argue about miracles, healing, tongues, and interpretation until the topics become so controversial the 'supernatural' can no longer be mentioned, or people leave churches who believe in 'that kind of stuff.' It breaks my heart that so many of my people choose playing it safe rather than risking to bless others." That's one of the differences between practicing a religion and following me." Jesus was clearly grieved, and sat for a few minutes as the group waited.

"Religion. It's what I fought while I was on earth, and it's what I'm still fighting today. By religion, I mean the practice of rituals and the propagation of doctrines and memberships in factions without the reality of the power of God. It drove my apostle Paul crazy, too. Remember when he wrote his first letter to the Corinthian church, in the second chapter? He said that his message and his preaching came not just in persuasive words of wisdom, but in demonstration of the Spirit and of power, so that their faith would not rest on the wisdom of men, but on the power of God. Later in the same letter, in chapter four, he told them that the kingdom of God does not consist in words but in power." Jesus gestured to the Bible sitting on the table.

"People who desperately need me usually seek me out among my people. Many times, however, instead of finding me and my loving power, they find only religion. They come for what I can give them only to be turned away. If they stay in these religious churches, they're told what they must believe differently than other 'supposed' Christians. Then they're told how to behave in order to be accepted. Finally, they're taught information, theology, and doctrine and then sent on their way. No wonder people become discouraged with the church, both inside and out. When I said, 'Go make disciples,' I didn't mean recruit members for religious institutions. I said to teach them ALL I had commanded. I promised to be present with my disciples always, so people could come to know me, experience my love, and live it out with others."

Jesus stood and looked at what had now become the fearful three, and said to them, "I want you to love people with my love in every place I lead you. Love them with the wisdom and knowledge that I give you. Care for their needs without the strings of 'come to my church' attached. When people do come to Emmaus Church, I want them to experience my love and my power. If they need healing, don't just pray for the doctor. That's a good thing to do, but I want you to minister healing to them. If they come confused, then minister words of knowledge and wisdom; don't just send them off to a good counselor. When people come to you harassed by the enemy, like you were last week, I want you to use your authority to drive the devil away and teach my beloved how to resist. If they need food, then feed them. When they become convinced that I am among you, then tell them the Gospel of Truth and invite them to receive me in faith."

Jesus looked intently at His dismayed friends. "I want the family of Emmaus Community Church to commune with me, as you have been learning to do. I want them to let my love and compassion for others flow through them, just as it has begun to flow through you. When people realize that I am actually present with you and that you know me and love me, then they will want to join you and discover how to know me too. It's really quite simple." Jesus sat down again and waited.

After a long silence, Jim responded. "Lord, some of that we can do. But we're not a charismatic church; we don't really know about miracles. We're afraid of their misuse. What You want sounds right; but for one, I don't feel up to it. It just feels like You're asking too much. I'm sorry, but that's how I feel." The others nodded agreement with Jim's sentiments of hopelessness and felt sorry that he seemed to be on the hot seat in this conversation.

Smiling, Jesus reached out, and put His hand on Jim's knee and said, "Jim, I understand your hesitation. I know it's much safer to conduct church in a human way. I know that you and your people haven't learned to use the gifts they've been given. I also agree that some people make mistakes and confuse their own thoughts and desires for mine." However, my followers are called, *you* are called, to minister in both words and deeds as signs of my Presence. I know that you have a lot to learn about wielding the sword of my Spirit, and there will always be more mystery to explore. But I must tell you, as I did my first disciples: if you love me, you will obey my commandments. If you want to follow me, you must also take up your cross—the very things that may get you rejected and ridiculed—and follow me."

Jesus sat silently, as the group tried to swallow the food He served them. Then He continued. "My beloved, I know that you love me and I recognize that you're frightened by what I'm asking. I also understand that you'd never trade what we've experienced together. I don't think you would deprive others of it, either. Together we can invite many to adoption, to discover abundant life and freedom from the tyranny of their fears. Together we can offer them transformation so that they may live fully and freely in my Kingdom and experience the amazing joy of sharing my victory. What I have given you, I'm asking you to give to others. As you step out to follow me, the Holy Spirit will help you remember all that I've said and teach you how to give my love and power away."

Jesus paused. Jim, Barry, and Lillian sat frozen in place, their minds swirling. Jim looked down while Barry and Lillian just stared at the wall. Jesus awaited an answer to an invitation that seemed frightening and way beyond their ability. He was asking them to join the ranks of saints and martyrs. In fact, He expected all believers to become saints and martyrs. But how could they dare? Yet He was right; they had experienced too much to ever return to their old lives. They could never look at another human being again without wishing for them what they had received from Jesus. They felt trapped between wanting to share the wonderful gift of Jesus' Presence, and bewildered by its seeming impossibility.

In a number of stages Jesus had asked them to follow Him. He asked them to follow Him into forgiveness and they responded willingly. He invited them to follow Him into abundant life and they gladly accepted. Jesus challenged them to experience His Presence beyond the ability of their senses, and they dared to experiment and learn about the journey of adoption and transformation. Jesus showed them their responsibility to share that opportunity with others, and they said they'd gladly follow Him in that mission. But now Jesus was asking them to follow Him into a new level of radical risk and radical trust, into the world of the Holy Spirit—to become knights of the King.

Jesus finally repeated the words that terrified them, "Barry, Lillian, Jim, will you follow me? Will you let me help you? Remember my promise that I will never leave you or forsake you. I will never ask you to do anything that we can't do together. Will you help Emmaus Church to recognize that I'm Present? When they come to experience me and come to believe in me and love me, will you teach them how to follow me, as I have taught you?"

Jesus stood up again and addressed them. "I have posed hard questions today. They're questions that you'll have to answer over again, every day of your lives. I'll always be present to be gladdened by your answer and ready to lead and empower you—as you say yes."

Jesus smiled at them and something in them knew that the wondrous and life-changing visitations had come to an end. Their hearts sank and tears welled. They wanted to jump up and scream, "No!" but all they could do was sit there, numb. Would it really end like this?

Jesus stepped toward Lillian who stood to receive His embrace. He whispered in her ear, "You will become a mother to many you don't yet know. You will show them the mother-love of God, and I will help you."

Then Jesus turned to Barry who also stood and stepped toward Jesus and threw his arms around Him. Deep sobs lay agonizingly silent within his heart as Jesus whispered in Barry's ear, "You will cultivate the fields of my Kingdom and plant seeds of love that will produce a thousand-fold, seeds that I shall give you."

Finally Jesus turned to Jim who stood motionless, as if frozen in time. "Jim, my son, open your heart to the winds of the Holy Spirit who will sweep you into my Presence so that we may shepherd together." Then, leaning closer, Jesus whispered in Jim's ear, "Just let me love you; the rest will come."

Jesus walked toward the door, then turned and faced His heart-struck followers, His hands outstretched. Jesus' robe began to shine like the sun and His eyes sparkled with fire-like brilliance. His face glowed with radiant love for them. His crown transformed from the simple golden three-peaked band to a beautifully jeweled halo whose light filled the room and seemed to radiate outward and upward through the walls and ceiling. They stood mesmerized in awe.

Lillian was the first to notice and quickly motioned to Jim and Barry to look. As Jesus' form slowly began to fade from their sight, there appeared what looked like spaces in His robe, emanating out from His chest. As they stared at His robe in amazement, it seemed as though they saw through clouds or mist into another world. While unable to discern anything distinctly, they gazed through Jesus into a reality beyond. They blinked, wondering if their minds were playing tricks. Beautiful high mountains, rivers, and cities of light seemed almost visible. In the midst of it all, a great throne that radiated a brilliant rainbow light, bathed the whole land in a beautiful radiance. As their eyes attempted to focus, they felt as if they were flowing through those spaces into great joy, wondrous love, and a freedom beyond words. The three gasped and turned their attention again to Jesus' eyes, which smiled and glistened with profound love. "See what I have for you?" they seemed to say. As Jesus disappeared from their sight they heard His voice deep within their hearts, "I love you; remember My Presence."

Chapter 13: What Now?

The group left the church in silence, feeling both exhilaration and terrible loss. On the one hand, they'd experienced Jesus in the flesh. They'd actually seen Him, touched Him, heard His voice, communicated back and forth, and come to know and love Him as a person, actually present with them. They'd been privileged to experience what millions of Christians longed to experience over thousands of years. Jim, Barry, and Lillian had received a profound healing from the scars of sin. They'd come to know themselves personally as the beloved sons and daughter of the Father of all creation, siblings of the King of Kings, and temples of the same Holy Spirit who moved upon the waters in creation and raised Jesus from the dead. A more wonderful experience than these past months with Jesus, even with all its challenges, would have been unimaginable.

Nevertheless, each one drove home with a terrible sense of abandonment and grief. God's wonderful explosion into their lives had ended. It was over. Jesus was gone. As much as they told themselves that He remained Present, they knew only in heaven would they physically feel His embrace, look into His eyes, and hear His voice in those physical soul-fired ways again. He'd led them to the mountaintop; but tonight, this valley felt more like a bottomless pit. What would happen now?

To further exacerbate their feelings of desolation, Jesus had deeply disturbed them in their last conversation. He openly shared His suffering for the world and His dreams for the

Church. They'd seen and felt His great passionate love for every person in the world and His longing for the Church to become the reality of His Presence. But their hearts grieved at their own fear and resistance to believe they could accomplish what Jesus desired. He yearned for everyone to receive the wonderful gift of adoption as sons and daughters and to experience transformation into mature and skilled knights of the Kingdom of God. But they felt small, insignificant, and powerless in the daunting shadow of that vision. With all their hearts they wanted to please their Lord, to make Him happy and proud of them. But fear gripped them, fear of the cost, fear of appearing foolish, fear of failure. He'd left them unable to return to the past and terrified of the future.

"Oh, God, what will happen now?" each prayed.

Barry returned home after the meeting, headed straight to the barn, and plopped on "their" bale of hay. In those midnight hours, no rays of sunlight shone through the window to encourage him. This loneliness felt even more painful than the agony of Elaine's death. Barry realized how, in these last months, he'd grown from a grouchy, self-pitying, critical loner into a man who genuinely loved people. He also recognized that each day had centered on his interactions with Jesus, both when they were together and in anticipation of when they would meet again. His relationship with God had been transformed from a disappointing religion to a vibrant relationship that opened up the amazing wonders of life and the coming Kingdom of God. In the depths of his heart, Barry's identity had become unhinged from the genealogy of his family and the piece of ground branded as his farm. While all those things remained as precious gifts, he now saw himself as the friend and brother of Jesus, an adopted son of The Most High God, on a mission with his Lord.

Yet he scolded himself that these changes could only have happened because Jesus came to him physically. His faith could never have received this amazing transformation on its own. Now that the "flesh and blood" Jesus had left him, he fully expected his faith to crumble again, leaving him worse off than before.

As Barry slipped from his sitting position atop the hay bale to the floor, feeling the rough stubbles of that sacred hay needling his back, sobs welled up from deep within him. A kind of convulsion of all his internal organs seemed to cry out to God, "Lord save me, for I am only a sinful man. Who am I to have seen the Lord? How can I live another day?" Barry fell asleep on the barn floor only to be awakened by the dim morning light and the agonizing absence of the One he had come to know and love as Present. "Now what?" he whispered.

ഔൽ ർൽ

Lillian, returned to her family room and spent the night in the "Jesus chair," where He'd sat on Thursday mornings, week after week. While she'd always known that these face-to-face encounters with Jesus would come to an end, she had consistently put the thought out of her mind. Now, however, this "end" filled and engulfed her whole being. Lillian replayed every encounter and every conversation over and over again in her mind, beginning with the near accident, ending with Jesus' "disappearance" only hours earlier.

She'd learned so much and her life had changed so drastically. Now His absence made her realize the extent to which every aspect of everyday had come to center around the Presence of Jesus. Knowing Him, really knowing Him personally, enlightened everything she thought and did. She'd become a better mother and wife as she learned to see her family though His eyes and with His love. New compassion for her church and the people around her flooded her life with meaning and purpose. But now what? This amazing miracle had evaporated into thin air, gone forever; she couldn't even imagine going back to her previous monotonous life. The future seemed nothing but a blur, a wall beyond which all real joy seemed obscured. Tears streamed down Lillian's cheeks and knots in her stomach threatened to choke her heart. "Jesus," she said over and over, half expecting Him to relent and appear next to her once more.

To make matters worse, Jesus had irrevocably intertwined her life with two men she would never have chosen—Pastor Jim and Barry Anderson, with whom she had nothing in common—other than Jesus. She wondered if she would see them again or if she even wanted to. Ultimately sleep captured and quieted Lillian's pain until a small voice broke the morning silence, "Mommy?"

ಶಿಶಿ ೧೩೧೩

Jim didn't go home after the meeting, but stayed at church. He turned off the lights in his office and found his way into the dark Sanctuary. Sitting in his "morning prayer-time pew," the shepherd of Emmaus Community Church sank into despair, guilt and confusion. His despair ached like he'd lost his best friend. Guilt arose from his sense of total incompetence to fulfill the challenge and mission Jesus had given him. Confusion rolled over him like a dense fog suffocating a stranded rowboat in the middle of the Atlantic. Like Lillian, he replayed all the events of this amazing and life-changing encounter with Jesus, but in the end he wondered why it had all happened. "Why did He pick me; why not the pastor of some mega-church with an international television ministry?" Jim sat motionless in the pew, his eyes staring into the cross in front of him, staring with blurred vision that sought to get lost in its object rather than see it clearly.

Jim tried to pray, but he couldn't; he didn't know what to say. The dense fog seemed to suffocate even a desire to reach out to God. He had to admit that he felt betrayed by Jesus for taking him onto the mountain and then shoving him over a cliff into free fall. He thought about Sunday and the sermon he had prepared. It all seemed so meaningless right now. Jesus had said that the church services felt more like memorial services than worship in His Presence. Jim felt like the next Sunday SHOULD be a memorial service. What would he say? "My best friend Jesus has just left me alone with an impossible mission. I feel abandoned and helpless. I don't want to be a pastor anymore." His head knew that wasn't true, but it expressed his feelings perfectly. After several hours of dark brooding, Jim drove home and slipped silently into bed and let sleep draw him into dark obscurity. He awoke early the next morning and found his pillowcase wet with tears. "What now?"

Strangely, these three followers of Jesus did not speak to one another for the next three weeks. Barry and Lillian sat in the pews as Jim preached on Sunday. But as soon as the service ended, the two quickly left from doors on opposite sides of the church, while their pastor busied himself with other people. They couldn't even exchange glances. Interestingly, they ignored Jesus as well. Early mornings found Barry doing chores rather than sitting reflectively on his hay bale. Lillian slept in until the kids woke her up. Jim decided that he needed to start running in the morning, leaving only enough time to shower and get into the office for his first meeting. Of course Jesus and the other two never left their minds, but they kept their grief buried deep enough to control the pain.

છ૪૭ ૦૪૦૪

But the Lord didn't leave them stalled forever. As had happened so many times before, the Holy Spirit used Barry to finally break the deadlock. Clarity came during chores on the fourth Thursday after their last meeting as he shoveled manure from the horse stall in the barn. Brow furrowed, he looked at the mare and said, "My life smelled just like this stall before Jesus. I gave up on God once before; damned if I'll do it again!" The horse looked at Barry with her big brown eyes that seemed to understand and agree.

After chores, Barry picked up the phone. "Pastor Jim, this is Barry. I'll be in your office at 7:30 PM tonight. Be there."

191

The phone went silent. Then Barry called Lillian whose phone went to a recording. "Lillian, you know who this is. I'm meeting Pastor Jim in his office tonight. We can't do this without you. Be there at the usual time."

All three hurriedly rearranged their schedules, and managed to meet in the church office precisely at 7:30 P.M., and took their seats. The pain in the room groaned like the silence of a wake. No one wanted to talk about the thoughts and feelings that had been throwing daggers within their hearts for the past three weeks, but their facial expressions and demeanor told the stories. Even if they had shared it all, they wouldn't have known what to say after that. Jim and Lillian thought, "What now?" With an almost overwhelming compulsion, Barry was thinking, "I have to do this now!"

After the long awkward silence, Barry cleared his hoarse voice with a few introductory ah's. "We just can't live this way. We'll dry up like a wheat field without water. The enemy will have a hay-day with us, literally. We've gotta get help."

Lillian stiffened in her chair and stared at the wall. "Help? We're no good to ourselves or each other and we can't tell anyone else, so how are we going to get help?"

"That's the way I feel," Jim added, "lost and scared."

Barry went on. "We all feel that way. But there's a Helper that we can turn to Who understands how we feel and is willing to help us. He can connect us again, to Jesus and to each other. We have to try."

The three sat in silence for what seemed like hours until Lillian responded. "You're right, Barry. It's what Jesus told us to do. He said that the Holy Spirit would connect us with Him and the Father. But I've felt so down and hurt and ashamed of myself. I've just wrapped myself in a dark cocoon and stayed there."

"Me too," Jim mumbled. "But we can't live this way; you're right, Barry."

Barry led as the three knelt, joined hands, and bowed their heads. Barry squeezed Jim's hand. "You're better with words."

Jim prayed out, "Dear Lord, Father, Jesus, Holy Spirit, we need your help. You know the funk we've been in—pure selfishness—but we feel stuck. We've tried to get rid of these feelings and shape up, but it hasn't worked. We ache without your physical presence, Jesus. You know how badly it hurts. We know You're here with us, even though it feels like You're on some other planet. We want to continue the mission You started with us, but we're frightened and don't know what to do next. Holy Spirit, You're the only One who can connect us with the Three of You, so we're asking You to fill us, comfort us, teach us, and bring us again to Jesus."

Time seemed to stand still in the town of Emmaus, as three of God's beloved sought His face, yearned for Him with all their hearts, and waited.

Softly and slowly, to their astonishment, an angelic song arose from within their hearts, repeating a simple song over and over in their minds:

"How wonderful are You,
our Lord God. How merciful
Your grace and beautiful
Your love. For You redeem
the hearts of Your followers
and lead them in Your
everlasting light. Hallelujah!"

No more words were spoken; no tears shed; no telling expressions. They felt only peace and—Presence.

After about five minutes, the three released their hands, opened their eyes, rose to their feet, and looked at one another. Lillian spoke first with a radiant smile. "I heard this song, as if an angelic choir were singing in a huge cathedral whose ceiling opened up to heaven itself. Then I think I felt His kiss on my cheek—not my physical face of course, but my "real" cheek. Do you know what I mean? The kiss communicated His peace and Presence without words or touch, and filled me with hope and love."

Barry looked up, eyes filled with tears, "I heard it too. After the angel choir, I imagined Johnny who rode the tractor with Jesus and me. He came and knelt next to me. I felt his hand clasp mine through yours, Jim. I didn't hear words, but I knew—I mean I know—that Jesus is treating me as tenderly as He did my little friend. It's not going to be scary or lonely; following Jesus is going to be fun."

Jim looked at his hand. It wasn't hard to believe what Barry experienced. He'd felt something happening as well, but had no idea what. Love just seemed to embrace his and Barry's hands tightly in a deep warmth. Jim then shared his own experience. "At first nothing seemed to happen. After a time, I felt a battle raging inside me. Something in me didn't want to connect with Jesus. A dark shadowy figure appeared, armed with a black sword. I saw the word 'Fear' engraved on its blade. To my surprise, the shadowy figure seemed to be fighting on my behalf, rather than attacking me. 'I'll protect you,' it rasped. As the dark figure struck out into the darkness with the black sword, another blade responded with lightning speed, mighty force and flashing light. Although I couldn't see the face of its wielder, I knew that Jesus held its handle. The inscription His blade read 'John 14.' Jesus conquered the shadowy figure and I felt the fear leave my body as though a million tiny bugs fled the dazzling light of God's love. I think I can say, maybe for the first time in my life, that I'm no longer afraid." Jim grinned with amazement and wonder. "Then, of course, the choir," Jim added with a smile.

Instinctively, Barry reached for the Bible on the table and opened it to the fourteenth chapter of John. He read the first verse and then passed the Bible on to Lillian who read the next. Lillian passed it on to Jim who read the next verse, and so on. Words and phrases seemed echo off the page into a chorus indelibly inscribed within their minds. This short chapter encapsulated all that the Lord had taught them and provided the treasure map to answer their question, "What next?"

Let not your heart be troubled; believe in God,
believe also in me
I will come again, and receive you to myself; that
where I am, there you may be also.
I am the way, and the truth, and the life;
the works that I do you shall do also; and greater
works than these shall you do.
And whatever you ask in my name, that will I do.
I will not leave you as orphans; I will come to you.
But the Helper, the Holy Spirit, whom the Father
will send in my name, He will teach you all things,
and bring to your remembrance all that I said to you.
Peace I leave with you; my peace I give to you.
Arise, let us go from here.

Barry, Lillian, and Jim spent the next hour recalling the particular phrases that seemed to speak to them. Jim grabbed his laptop and recorded their thoughts making three copies for study and prayer. They covenanted together to find quality personal time each day for prayer, spending the time just being with Him and listening, waiting for Him to set the agenda. Each Thursday evening they'd meet and learn from what each one experienced during the previous week.

They left the office and passed through the church Sanctuary. Moonlight bathed the stained glass windows and soft colors filled the room. Instinctively, their eyes scanned the room in hope they'd see Him.

"What now?" Jim whispered.

Jim, Barry, and Lillian each sought to find a full hour daily to spend attentively with Jesus, determined to experience Him as truly Present, even if not physically. Jim kept his morning time at church, but decided to take Jesus' rocking chair into the Sanctuary, and imagine Him sitting there. The early morning light streaming through the stained glass windows helped him remember that the Kingdom of God had come to earth in Jesus and that the Throne of God stands present to everyone. Jim found it easier to sense Jesus' Presence when he closed his eyes and listened. When his mind wandered, he would open his eyes and look again at the chair and say something like, "I'm back, Lord."

Barry experimented with his prayer time by sitting on the hay bales in the barn, riding on the tractor, and finally found that walking with Jesus down the road or across the field felt most satisfying. He would usually begin the walk by asking Jesus, "Where to today, Lord?" Then he'd follow his first instinct and walk in that direction. Occasionally, Barry would imagine Jesus actually walking inside him, enjoying the fertile earth, warm sunshine or cold rain.

Lillian liked the family room where she'd always met with Jesus. She tried sitting in her chair and imagining Jesus sitting in His, but the room still felt empty to her. Finally she tried sitting in Jesus' chair. She used the exercise that Jesus taught them in Pastor Jim's office by imagining Jesus physically sharing the same space with her. While she didn't feel, see, or hear anything physically, at times she did sense the deep interior Presence of the Lord. She held on to the truth that He remained present with her whether she sensed it or not.

Each of them began their prayer times by talking to Jesus, telling Him what they were feeling and thinking, describing the challenges of the day. In time, however, each one remembered the pattern that Jesus had used with them in their physical meetings. Jesus would enter the room and immediately establish the line of conversation. He already knew what was going on, so He didn't need to be informed. So now, after beginning with some informal greeting to the Lord, they would remain silent and attentive. They knew that they probably wouldn't audibly "hear" anything from Jesus, but that His thoughts would come to them from within. They also worked at recognizing their own feelings and thoughts without having to put words to them, all the while attentive to the Holy Spirit's indication of the line of discussion the Lord wanted to take. They had learned that Jesus usually met them in the context of the activities of the day or the topic that they'd been discussing with one another. In time, they learned to trust Jesus to guide their thinking and recognized the difference between distractions or mind wandering and the truth of His subtle guidance.

They also learned that Jesus wanted to impress insights upon their subconscious that weren't apparent to them at the time. While in a given prayer time, it may have seemed that no real exchange took place. Only later might they realize that God had spoken to them about the current matter in their earlier times of prayer. For example, Lillian had spent her morning time with Jesus sitting in His chair. Most of that time she'd said nothing and sensed nothing from the Lord. She did, however, find Walter coming to mind. He would be returning from a business trip that afternoon and be home for the weekend. As she sat with Jesus, she became aware of how much she loved Walter and looked forward to having her family together. Later that day, when Walter did come home, Lillian greeted him with a warm hug and kiss, but at the same time stayed particularly attentive to her own feelings. Without really planning to, she said to Walter, "Honey, you look really tired and stressed. Have you had a rough day? Why don't I pour us a glass of wine before dinner while you greet the kids. We'll let them finish their Veggie Tales, and we can talk."

Walter looked surprised and responded, "You're pretty perceptive, young lady! I almost quit my job today and I really do need to talk. Thanks for being so sensitive."

"Thanks, Lord," Lillian whispered to Jesus. "You prepared me in our prayer time this morning."

All three also noticed how Jesus seemed to highlight certain parts of their thinking during prayer. With all that had been going on, their minds were filled with questions, doubts, and fears about what it would mean to follow Jesus going forward. Barry, for example, kept asking Jesus, "What do you want me to do now?" but received no discernable response. However, he noticed his thoughts returning to the men at the bar he'd interviewed some months before and wondered how people like that could ever learn to experience Jesus as Present.

While Jim prayed, he noticed how often he thought of Jesus "up" in heaven, even with the rocking chair right in front of him. He prayed, "Turn my mind and heart, O Lord, to know You—Present, just like before"

They also learned to test their insights and experiences against the truths of Scripture. Jesus would never guide them in ways contrary to the clear teachings of the Bible. So, when fears or negative thoughts about someone came to mind, for example, they knew they hadn't come from the Lord.

For several weeks they faithfully kept their morning prayer times. They met on Thursday evenings to discuss their discoveries about relating to Jesus as Present. Barry's comment summed up much of their experience: "When I try to make something happen, I can't sense Jesus. But when I relax and just enjoy being with Him, all sorts of things come to mind and lines of thought take shape that I'm sure came from Him. When I trust Him to be Present, I experience His Presence!"

Toward the end of their fifth evening meeting since Jesus had "disappeared," Lillian spoke up. "I think we're all learning to 'just be' with the Lord and trust His Presence. In subtle ways, He's speaking to us and guiding us. But I also need to share about what He seems to be saying to me about the future, about what's next. Frankly, I'm confused and a bit frightened."

Barry and Jim raised their eyebrows and responded almost simultaneously, "You too?"

They agreed to meet again the next week.

Chapter 14: Discoveries

"The rocking chair! Where's the rocking chair?" Barry demanded.

Lillian chimed in, "Yeah, Jim, what did you do with the rocking chair? It'll feel really strange to meet without that chair."

"Sorry!" Jim raised his hands defensively. "I left it in the Sanctuary where I have morning prayer. I'll get it right now. Meanwhile, you guys can make the tea," Jim grinned as he walked out of the office.

Soon they were settled again; the rocking chair in its place, and tea in hand. "I sure miss the scones," Lillian moaned. "I thought of making some myself, but I can't compete with the Lord's multi-flavors."

"Don't you worry," Barry chuckled. "Yours will taste just fine. I think we'll all enjoy whatever you make."

As had become their custom, the group knelt as Jim prayed, "Thanks, Jesus for being here with us, for Your love and forgiveness, for Your patience with us, and for Your persistent shepherding of our lives. We love You and dedicate our conversation to you and look forward to your guidance and participation. Amen, hallelujah."

Returning to their seats, they began checking in about what they'd experienced the previous week. But soon after they'd begun, Barry interrupted in a frustrated tone. "All this general sharing stuff is great and I've really appreciated it, but I'm about to explode with the need to DO something! You mentioned it last week, Lillian. I have the feeling that Jesus wants me, at least, to get off my butt and get to work! But I need your help to put the pieces together."

Lillian reached over and put her hand on Barry's knee. "You're right, Barry. I have the same sense. That's what I was trying to say at the end of our meeting last week. I'm just not clear about what the Lord's telling me. I keep waiting for Jesus to lay it all out."

Jim jumped in. "I sure appreciate your honesty, both of you. I've felt the same way, but the direction I'm sensing for me seems so impossible that I feel paralyzed. I don't know where to even start."

After a long pause, Jim continued. "Let's each take some time to get what we're struggling with out on the table so we can all see what we're dealing with. I agree that Jesus threw us in this thing together, so chances are we need each other to figure out how to follow Him. Barry, why don't you begin?"

Barry cleared his throat, looked at the rocking chair and said, "You gotta help me with this Lord." He gulped some tea to wet his throat and turned to Lillian and Jim. "I keep remembering the instructions the Lord gave us that last night we were all together. I don't know if you heard, but He whispered to me: 'You will cultivate the fields of my Kingdom and plant seeds of love that will produce a thousand fold, seeds that I shall give you.' I have no idea what that really means or how that's going to happen through a thickheaded farmer like me. But before I can figure that out, I need to process some thoughts whirling around in my head."

Jim and Lillian took sips of tea and nodded their invitation for Barry to continue.

Barry stood up and began to pace back and forth, half looking at the ceiling and half searching the floor. He paced and mumbled to himself for several minutes trying to collect his thoughts. He wished he'd taken notes, but he hadn't. Finally he blurted out, "Okay, I'm just going to think out loud. I'm no theologian so don't go setting my words straight; it'll only distract me." Jim and Lillian both glanced at each other with a smile and then pinched their lips in a promise to keep quiet.

Barry continued, "Jesus wants us to help people experience Him as present with them. That's all well and good if people want that. But I don't think most people really want Him around at all. They just don't feel worthy, or put another way, having Jesus too close would only make them feel guilty. People just don't understand God's grace and love. They think they have to be good enough to be close to Jesus, much less get adopted into His family. Six months ago, if you'd asked me if I wanted Jesus riding the tractor with me, I'd have run from the idea. Who would want Mister Perfect sitting there pointing out all your mistakes or bringing up what you did or didn't do the day before? People gotta discover that God loves them even though they smell a bit like manure, and wants to help them in the midst of whatever's going on in their lives."

Jim broke his promise and interrupted, "I think you're right, Barry, but I preach about God's love almost every Sunday."

"I'm not talking about church, Jim; I'm talking about life. Besides most of the folks I'm thinking about don't come to church. Nope. They have to learn it by experience, just like we did. People will believe it's true when they experience it as true. It's up to us to show them, not just tell them. How the he__, uh, dickens are we going to do that? So that's the first thing rumbling around in my head."

The pacing back and forth continued as Barry plowed forward. "The other question sticking in my craw has to do with this business of adoption. Remember how Jesus taught us about adoption and transformation. Most folks have no idea what that's about. They understand about believing things, maybe belonging to a church, even having friends who would pray for them. But the idea that God wants to adopt us as His kids, accept us at our worst, and give us all the privileges of His throne isn't even imaginable to the normal person on the street. What in the world would that look like? Do you get a new birth certificate, access to an unending bank account or what? You and I know it means to be loved by the Father, Son, and Holy Spirit. It means having His protection and guidance. It means never having to be afraid again. But remember that the whole business about adoption and transformation became real to us, I mean we really understood it, as we got to know Jesus in practical ways. I think people have to experience that way, as well."

Barry paused just long enough to catch his breath. "Adoption means living in a family that we can depend upon. Look at us. We're the last threesome one would expect to become a family with Jesus. We've got different backgrounds, interests, talents, and opinions. Remember that first night Jesus brought us together? We were all devastated. But now we truly love each other and respect one another. That happened because Jesus loved us and connected us. In the safety of His Presence, we could share honestly and listen to one another without being defensive, discovering the real person that Jesus loves in each of us. We bonded together in Jesus. Loving Him in common came to mean more than all our differences. We experienced adoption into God's family as He taught us how to live with Him as Lord and with each other as brothers and sister. Adoption has to be sampled or tasted in real life before people can really get it. How do we enable that to happen?"

Barry paced and talked faster and faster, as his volume rose and his hands waved. "That brings me to my final issue, at least for tonight. It's one thing to be told that God loves you when you don't feel so lovable, but it's another thing to really believe it. All my life I've heard that God loves me. Yet, especially with the way I felt about Him after what Elaine went through, you'd have had a hard time making me believe it. Maybe the way I reacted showed that I'd never really believed it in the first place. I would never have believed that either of you could love me until you demonstrated it with your patience and understanding day after day. Love isn't just an emotional feeling, but that's what people think. So what if God loves you from way up there someplace? It's nice if He feels kindly about you, but what practical difference does it make? Other people function the same way we do; they have to experience it; they have to know His Presence to realize that they can't live without His love. If Jesus won't appear to folks physically, then they need to experience His love through us. Once they know what God's love feels like, then they'll want to taste the Presence of Jesus."

Barry started to sit, then jumped up again. "I guess there's one more thing I need to add. The people that keep coming to my mind aren't so much the church folks, but the men I interviewed in the bars and prisons. People at church at least have access to the truth, but these outsiders feel as though they don't belong, don't fit in. They're not going to come to church to hear your best sermons, Jim. How will they discover Jesus as Present?" Barry plopped in his chair with a thud of finality and exhaustion.

Jim responded first. "You're right, Barry. You can see the same principle in the Book of Acts. People didn't start by joining a religious group. They experienced the reality of Jesus in His followers. They recognized that He lived because of the way His followers loved them and the amazing things that happened when the disciples prayed. Then they accepted an invitation to visit a home church and learn more. That's what I've wanted for our church for a long time, but I have to agree that I don't know how to get there, either."

The three sat silently, pondering what Barry had said and Jim's reflections about the disciples. Finally, Lillian spoke up. "You know, Barry, I can't say that I have any answers either, but I find myself quite encouraged."

"How's that?" Barry mumbled and shook his head. Jim looked at Lillian with the same question.

"I'm excited about what the Lord's been telling you. I'm moved by the way you've taken it to heart, and I'm hearing

Jesus' heart in you as well. You really do care about these people and what keeps them from the Lord. I guess I'm also encouraged because I know that the Lord wouldn't move you in this way unless He intended to do something about it. Barry, I think you're the best man I know to team with Jesus about this. We all need to pray for ongoing insight into what the Lord wants you, and us, to do. I know it seems impossible, but has the Lord ever left us in the lurch so far?"

Barry pulled himself out of his chair and reached out to Lillian and gave her a hug. "Thanks for the encouragement. I can't imagine even considering all this without the both of you."

After a refill of tea, Lillian shared her own reflections. "Well, guys, Barry isn't the only one who's been struggling with what to do next. I agree with all the difficulties of getting there that you mentioned, Barry. These last few weeks I've been haunted by what Jesus asked from us, too. I think that even if people do want to experience Jesus as a real person, present with them, most of them don't have a clue about how to discern His Presence. Most of the Christians I know don't really believe that God speaks to people today, or if He does, it only happens through the printed pages of the Bible. Remember how Jesus had to patiently take us by the hand and show us step by step how to listen with our hearts and how much we needed each other to help interpret what we thought we experienced? Where in church life do we teach people how to recognize Jesus—or that it is even possible? We all need to learn what it means to abide in Jesus. In fact, I'm discovering that 'abiding in the vine' provides the best analogy for understanding prayer, both talking and listening. We couldn't have taught a class about that kind of prayer at church because we didn't even understand it ourselves. But someone has to teach people how to experience Jesus personally. Actually, I think lots of people hunger for a real relationship with Jesus, both in and outside the church."

"You're right, Lillian," Jim responded. But, I think I'd have trouble risking a class like that. It's one thing to teach biblical truths. I know the answers or where to find them. But teaching people to relate to Jesus in real time, well, He's so unpredictable. You both know that we never knew what He would do. There just isn't a neatly worked out system where we do this and Jesus will always do that."

Barry broke in. "There's truth in that, Jim. But Jesus does make promises in the Bible, promises that we've experienced as true. For example, He says that His sheep will hear His voice. That's not just a possibility; that's a promise! It just takes transformation of the ears of our hearts and the time, experimentation, and patience to learn how to use our new ears, but it's possible."

"There's more," Lillian continued. "People don't understand that they have to grow up spiritually as part of learning to hear His voice. Remember our situations when Jesus first came to us? Each one of us had so many issues to deal with in our relationship with God as well as how we understood ourselves. Sure, there were lots of sweet times with Jesus, but don't forget when we were all ready to bail on Him, too. We had, and still have, a lot of growing up to do."

"There must be ways we can describe the process of spiritual growth. The Bible uses lots of analogies. For example, Jesus talks about His disciples moving from servanthood into friendship and then on into the relationship as His beloved. The apostle Paul speaks of some people needing milk-type teaching and others ready for "meat" material. John also talks about children, young men, and fathers, comparing them to stages in the journey of spiritual maturity."

Lillian paused, gulped some now-cold tea, and went on before Barry or Jim could comment. "Surely someone in Christian history has expounded on those passages and suggested what that kind of spiritual growth looks like. Jesus taught us that transformation comes after adoption. We have to learn what that process looks like in real life so we can help others grow up spiritually."

Jim cut in, "That takes a lifetime, Lillian. We strive to be like Christ, but we never get there. But you're right. Spiritual growth means more than learning more biblical facts or getting our doctrine down. Jesus used the example of the young boy who became a knight and all that he had to learn. It wasn't so much about facts or skill; he had to learn to follow his King."

"That's right where we are now," Barry blurted out. "Jesus has adopted us and taught us; but now we're learning how to hear and follow our King. It does take more than knowledge; it takes guts—guts to follow Jesus. Courage like that comes from learning through experience that He's trustworthy. Trusting God only comes through the school of hard knocks, in the hands of the Holy Spirit. We have to fail a few times to experience that He does in fact work all things together for good for those that love Him and are called into His plan."

Before Lillian could continue, Barry lifted his finger for permission to keep going. "There's another part of the transformation you're talking about, Lillian. Some of us need healing before we can progress. I'm a good example. Before Jesus and I could get anywhere, I had to deal with my wounded heart about losing Elaine and the anger I felt toward the Lord. I think a lot of people struggle with things like that. Our hearts can be hardened through events that hurt us and a hard heart resists Jesus rather than seeks Him. It's like asking someone with broken leg to drive a tractor! So, I'm right with you, Lillian. You're onto an important part of this whole picture. There's a lot to learn about ourselves and the Lord as we are transformed and enabled to discern His Presence." Barry sat back in his chair and said to the rocking chair, "Right?"

Lillian and Barry turned to Jim and said together, "You're up. How is Jesus getting under your skin?"

But Jim objected. "Lillian, I'm curious about what the Lord whispered in your ear that last night."

Lillian blushed and responded, "Well, I'm a little embarrassed to say. It sounds presumptuous."

"Don't be silly, Lillian. After what I shared about what He said to this old farmer, how could anything be more presumptuous than that?"

"Okay, okay. Here's what the Lord whispered. 'You will become a mother to many you don't yet know. You will show them the mother-love of God, and I will help you.'" She paused. "The words are imprinted on my mind as if He's written them on a plaque and hung it inside my skull. But I honestly have no idea what that means. I hope it doesn't mean Walt and I are going to have more kids!"

Barry and Jim smiled at her jest, but Jim pursued her. "What do you think it might mean, Lillian?"

Lillian paused for several minutes while Jim and Barry gave her space to think. Finally she replied, "I've wondered if it's about what's been on my mind—what I've been sharing. Seems to me that God calls the moms in the family to teach kids how to relate to others. We first experience bonding with our mothers. It's usually our mothers who teach us about intimacy and love. Issues about sharing toys and behaving respectfully often gets left to the moms. Do you think Jesus suggested that in some way I would help others learn how to bond with Him and know His love?"

Barry jumped right in with a broad grin, quoting Lillian's encouragement to Barry earlier in the discussion. "Lillian, I think that you're the best woman I know to do something with Jesus about it," His face reflected the sincerity of his statement.

Lillian grinned sheepishly and turned to Jim. "Okay, Jim. Now it's really your turn."

Jim sat silently for some time and then got up and lifted the rocking chair and headed toward the office door. "Come on. For me to get this out, we've got to move the location of the discussion." Barry and Lillian followed Jim down the hallway and into the Sanctuary. Jim turned on all the lights and then placed the rocking chair on the chancel, pulled three chairs near the rocker, and motioned for the others to sit down.

"Now sit here with me and look out across the pews. Imagine the congregation sitting there most Sunday mornings. They're the backdrop for what I need to share. I know Jesus wants this church, all churches for that matter, to become a community that actually experiences Him as Present. He told us that our experiences here need to model how each of us relate to Him every day. I get that, but that's way easier said than done. In fact, I don't have a clue how to go about it." Jim paused looking into his lap and then went on. "Well, I actually do have some clues, but think I'd get fired if I tried any of them."

Barry prompted him. "So, what are your clues, Jim?"

"Well, it seems to me that just about everything we do needs to change. Think about it. We all come in and greet one another. No one greets Jesus or even thinks about doing it. We open the service with a hymn or praise song about God rather than using the song to worship Him. We read some Scripture and hear a sermon about what the book says and how to apply that to our lives today. I think most people listen for what the preacher thinks about the passages rather than listening with their hearts for what Jesus may be saying to them personally. Sure, sometimes an insight gets through, but seldom do folks consider those words to be an encounter with Jesus' Presence. After the message, we say prayers as if sending them by long range transmitter to some other planet and close the service with another song about God or our theology. We fill every moment of the time with our talking or singing or praying, but never take time to hear anything from Jesus. Why should we? We don't expect to."

"Sounds about right. What would you do differently?" Barry questioned.

Jim got to his feet and started walking to different spots on the chancel as though he were practicing his thoughts as he shared them. "I'm not sure, but it may be more about <u>how</u> we do things than <u>what</u> we do. Nothing in our service seems that wrong; it just needs focusing—we just need focusing." He walked out into the rows of pews and continued, "Maybe people should start their time in church with some silence, affirming Jesus' Presence and their love for Him." Strolling back to the center of the chancel, he went on, "What if our opening prayer acknowledged that He abides right here with us, and we invited Him to lead our worship and speak to us? What if the songs we picked spoke directly to God rather than about Him?" Jim stepped behind the pulpit. "Could we use our imaginations and put ourselves into the Gospel story for the day, reflect on it in the message, and then be still for a bit to sense what the Lord might be saying to us personally?"

"What if…. Oh, I could go on and on, but people wouldn't understand. This church has used essentially the same service since its founding. We've updated some of the music and language, but that's all. People like the same old thing; it feels comforting. They just wouldn't understand why I started changing things." Jim plopped in his chair with a sigh.

Looking at Barry, Jim went on, "Like you said, people feel like Jesus resides on some other planet; that the right hand of God exists "up there" or "out there" somewhere. The Scriptures tell us clearly that the Kingdom of God is at hand, among us, within us! How do we convince our congregation, much less the rest of the folks out there, that Jesus lives right here with us so that they'll expect to meet Him personally?"

Barry responded, "Like I said, I think that people get it when their experience matches what they're being taught. We can't just tell people things and expect them to accept it at face value—not anymore."

"That's another thing," Jim stood up and started pacing again. "The world we live in exhibits a lot of hostility toward the church and its teachings. People consider us judgmental bigots, because we believe that some behaviors are right and moral and others are wrong and hurt people. This generation wants to do and believe whatever they want and can get really hostile when someone calls them on it. We've got the same problem within the church. People have their individual idea about what church should be like. Some want this and others want that. Most come as religious consumers. Everyone's after something different. Some look for a dynamic youth program. Others expect to be entertained with great music or oratorical preaching. Some want things casual for the younger folks and others like it more formal for the older ones. Instead of listening to what Jesus wants, we take votes and assume the majority knows what's right. We're here for us, not for Jesus!"

Jim plunked down in his chair and gasped, "Sorry for being so negative and overstating everything, but that's how I feel."

"Feels pretty hopeless, doesn't it?" Lillian said, putting her hand on Jim's shoulder.

Barry responded less tenderly. "Well, so far they're not feeding us to lions. If Jesus could handle that century, I'd guess He's not too worried about ours."

Lillian sighed, "It's not all your problem, Jim. It's not your job to change the church. We're a community here at Emmaus, even if we're not all on the same page. You're called to provide leadership as part of the Elders, and I'm part of the Elder Board, too. I think we have to begin there. Jesus started with us and we need to expand the circle. No, we can't tell the others what we've experienced, but we can teach them the Scriptures and encourage them to experiment. I agree with Barry. People have to experience the truth, not just be told about it. Even after our months with Jesus, face to face, we had to experiment and learn to experience Him as Present. Why should it be any different with others? Once the Elders begin to experience Jesus as Present in the Elder room, they'll be the ones clamoring to change the way we do church on Sunday mornings. Jim, you need to lead, but Jesus has provided Barry and me to help you and back you up. The Elders really do want an alive and vibrant relationship with Jesus. Let's give them a chance."

"She's right, you know Jim," Barry added. The Elder Board has focused almost entirely on the business of the church. We've never addressed our collective responsibility to lead the church under the shepherding of Jesus. I understand there's an opening on the Elder Board. What if I applied?"

"Some months ago I wouldn't have liked that idea very much, Barry. But now I would really appreciate the help. The Lord has given you both a deep wisdom and I need you; the church needs you."

Jim changed the subject. "It's getting late. Maybe we should continue our discussions next week. I thought we might…."

"No way, mister Pastor!" Lillian frowned a contrived frustration. "What did the Lord whisper to you that last night?"

Like the others, Jim felt shy about sharing something so personal and mysterious. Raising his eyebrows his mind seemed to leave the room and then he repeated the words slowly, 'Jim, my son, open your heart to the winds of the Holy Spirit who will sweep you into my Presence so that we may shepherd together.'" He paused, as tears welled in his eyes. "But He really got to me when He spoke again. He whispered, 'Just let me love you; the rest will come.' His last statement really nails where I struggle. Even after all I have experienced with Jesus, I still have trouble accepting that He really loves me— loves me enough to guide me through all this."

Lillian and Barry rose and enclosed Jim in an embrace. Barry spoke for both of them, "We wrestle with the same struggle, Jim. Maybe everybody does. But we're in this with you."

After they were seated again, Lillian turned to Jim, "I think you were about to make a suggestion before I interrupted you."

Jim responded, "Oh yeah, I had an idea. What if we meet the next few times in different places? When we unpack how the Lord seems to be leading you, Barry, we could meet at your farm. Lillian, it would be great to join you in your family room where you and Jesus met and hear more about what's going on in your heart. We can meet sometimes here at church, as well, but from what I'm hearing, Jesus' vision for us takes us way beyond the scope of this building. Maybe the variety would help us get some greater perspective."

Jim paused, smiled, and then continued, "Let's ask the Lord about it."

They pulled their chairs together, including the rocking chair. They then began a discernment process that Lillian had read about, one that the early church fathers had used. First, they sat silently for several minutes, just letting their love for God flow out and receiving His love within, all without words. Following the silence, Barry prayed for the group.

"Lord, deciding where we meet sounds like a simple thing, maybe trivial, but we want to follow Your leading specifically. Only You know what needs to happen among us, so we want to do it Your way. We relinquish our personal opinions, our preferences, our fears, and our hopes and we surrender ourselves to You as completely as we can. We confess that we're sinners, saved and forgiven through your death on the cross. You've redeemed us and called us to follow You. Please speak to our hearts and give us the peace that passes understanding when we have discerned Your will. Amen."

As Barry prayed about confession, each one silently let the issues that came to mind go to Jesus and pictured their sins like rocks at the foot of His cross. As they imagined their future meetings at various places, they watched for the sense of peace, or contrarily that of agitation or disquiet. Then they imagined meeting at church in the pastor's office with the rocking chair. When each one imagined a scene involving leaving the rocking chair behind, they felt fearful. They also recalled that Jesus resided with them and that while the rocking chair proved a good reminder, it couldn't become a crutch. They remembered that fear never comes from God. After about five minutes, Jim cleared his throat and quietly asked, "Are we ready to check in?"

Barry and Lillian sat forward in their chairs and nodded. Each one shared special experiences in time of prayer. All three reported that they'd felt a sense of peace as they imagined themselves meeting in various places, as Jim had suggested. They also reported not feeling that same peace when they contemplated staying solely in the office. Lillian put it this way. "When I imagined having you all at my house, I immediately thought about the kids and what I'd do with them. But then I told the Lord if that's what He wants, He'd show me how to get some help. I imagined us sitting in the family room, as you suggested, Jim, and it felt good and inviting. When I imagined us safely clustered around the rocking chair in your office or out here in the Sanctuary, I felt sort of claustrophobic. It didn't feel right."

Jim and Barry shared similar experiences and they agreed to expand their meeting places to get a better feel for how Lord might want to guide them.

Lillian looked at Barry, and Jim said, "Barry, I think we're to meet in your barn next. What do you think?"

Barry nodded with a broad smile. "I was going to suggest that."

Again, Jesus had confirmed His Presence by speaking to their hearts and confirming His words through the affirmation of the others. No one had prepared an agenda or planned a strategy; they just followed their inner senses which seemed to be running along the same line. They left the church that night with renewed confidence that the assignment Jesus had given them might not be as impossible as it first felt. But none of them could possibly have guessed the miracles that lay poised, waiting to surprise and bless them.

Chapter 15: Presence Unfolding

Ten years later to the day that Jesus first appeared to the three and changed their lives, Pastor Jim, Lillian, and Barry stood together in a wide open space on Barry's farm holding hands. Hundreds of people stood around them as they all sang songs of praise and worshiped God. Video cameras stood poised on tripods as the media worked to capture the scene and document its story. News about Emmaus had spread.

Of course most of what happened couldn't be told in the documentary, but the results have been recognized by all of Emmaus and far beyond. People from many Christian backgrounds have heard about the transformations that have taken place in the whole community and want to find out more.

As they had discussed, the three did meet at Barry's farm, in Lillian's family room, and in the office and church Sanctuary after Jesus had stopped meeting with them physically. They continued to discuss and discern the passions that the Lord had stirred up within them. Their meetings always intertwined serious discussion, lively brainstorming, laughter, disagreement, and always a time on their knees seeking the feelings, insights, questions, and the will of Jesus. These meetings continue in various forms, and with various people, to this day.

Over these ten years, much has changed their lives, accompanied by many trials and restarts that challenged their resolve. But the Lord led them and taught them faithfully, developing an amazing tapestry of the Lord's Presence.

The Order of Christ's Presence

Jim, Barry, and Lillian realized in the beginning that they couldn't follow Jesus in the way that He wanted without a close-knit community of fellow followers who understood the reality of Jesus' Presence and who knew how to listen to Him. They recognized that change takes time and usually meets significant resistance. Not the three nor anyone else would prove successful in bringing about significant transformation without being part of a group that had been personally called together by Jesus to follow Him in His plan for Emmaus. This group had to share common values, common calling, and a lifestyle that supported their ongoing spiritual growth. But who and how?

In the following months, a radical idea emerged out of one of their talk-and-prayer times. As they discussed the kinds of relationship and support they would need from each other, Jim commented that what they needed sounded a lot like what has historically been called an "order"—people with a common life calling and vision to love and serve Jesus, a common way of life, and common commitments to one another. Of course there would be some significant differences between their group and most historical orders. For example, they wouldn't necessarily live together; the Order would include both men and women, married and single; and they wanted their group to be interdenominational, based solely on the love of Jesus.

After considerable prayer and discernment, the three became convinced that Jesus was leading them to form such an Order. They then developed a covenant or set of agreements and commitments that they would make to one another. The covenant addressed aspects of their relationships such as how often they would meet, openness and honesty with one another and others, daily prayer for the members, and the subjection of every aspect of their lives to the authority and direction of Jesus. They would meet at least weekly for prayer, sharing life experiences, discerning the Lord's leading, and celebrating His Presence. Based on their covenant, they hammered out a Rule of Life which described the spiritual practices that they each would follow in their personal lives. Their Rule included spiritual disciplines designed to help them remain attentive to Jesus' Presence and to enable them to grow in their faith.

From the beginning, the three recognized that the new Order of Christ's Presence was not just for them, that Jesus would bring others to join them. He had given them a grand vision to live out His love for all the world, but they knew full well that they didn't have all that it would take to follow Him faithfully. They would need other personalities, skills, and perspectives grounded in a personal and dynamic relationship with Jesus. But they also recognized that everyone that might become associated with what God planned for Emmaus would be traveling their own journey of spiritual growth and may not be ready for the level of commitment that such an Order required. Jesus would make the connections if and when it became right, so they agreed not to be too quick to encourage others to join.

The Order remained just the three of them for about two years. Then one day, when Jim described the group's relationship in one of the Ministerial meetings, Father Pat expressed interest. He shared the similarity between his own Rule of Life and the one the Order had fashioned. He longed for a community of peers with whom to discuss and explore experiencing Jesus's Presence. Later that month, the Baptist pastor shared some of the same feelings with Jim. He visited the group for several months and eventually affirmed their covenant and committed to their Rule of Life. The Order slowly grew, adding Barry's two sons and Lillian's husband, Walter. Later, more came.

What proved significant about the Order of Christ's Presence wasn't related to any authority it possessed or some organizational influence, but its life of prayer. Most Christians in town have heard about the Order, nicknamed OCP, usually through a friend's story about the group's support and prayer for them in a time of need. The community soon recognized that when they needed wisdom or wanted to mobilize the faith community in Emmaus, OCP proved to be the place to start. The Order of Christ's Presence published no documents, held no conferences, nor established any long-range plans or mission strategies. They simply met for mutual support, encouragement, and prayer. Leadership rotated every year. While ordinary folks made up its membership, no one doubted that Jesus made His Presence known in profound ways when they sought Him there.

The Fellowship for Knowing Jesus

Years ago, Lillian shared with Walter about the new relationship she'd been experiencing with Jesus and what she'd learned about relating to Him as Present. Soon they began to pray together about their family and the activities of daily life, waiting for Jesus to teach and guide them. Lillian poured out her desire to learn more about the process of spiritual growth and to help people learn how to let Jesus connect with them in practical ways. At Walter's encouragement, and with Jim and Barry's affirmation, Lillian participated in a spiritual formation program at a seminary not too far away and received her Master's Degree.

Lillian was amazed by the number of people she met in her Master's program who were also hungry to know Jesus as Present. As her classmates shared their stories, she would love to have asked them if Jesus had appeared to them, as He had to her. While she would never have asked and knew that if He had, they would never have admitted it, she saw that each one had encountered Jesus in various ways. Some had become interested by overhearing discussions about spiritual formation and deeper intimacy with God. For others, their awakening had come through some difficulty or trial that caused them to cry out to the Lord for help, realizing that they needed to learn how to become attentive to His Presence and leadership.

Many roadblocks obstructed and delayed Lillian's progress, however. Most of her friends and members of her church had never heard of spiritual direction or they associated it only with Catholic monasteries. One friend expressed fear that Lillian planned to leave Emmaus Church and join St. Timothy's. Lillian fought continually against the assumption that only pastors and priests or maybe monks or nuns could give spiritual counsel. It took the active support of Father Pat and Pastor Jim to quell the opposition to Lillian's studies and planned role in the community.

She began providing spiritual direction to the increasing numbers of people affected by the changes that were happening in Emmaus. After graduation, she worked with the seminary to train others in spiritual direction, counseling, and mentoring. Eventually the needs became so great that a group led by Lillian formed to purchase an old deserted mansion on the edge of town. They desired to provide space for extended and day retreats as well as counseling, spiritual direction, and spiritual growth—in an atmosphere of quiet and peace.

Lillian and her family have moved and, after extensive renovation by volunteers, now live in the "servant quarters" of that large historic mansion. People have come to know the mansion as the Fellowship, short for "The Fellowship for Knowing Jesus." Walter now works from their home at the Fellowship using his phone and computer to carry out his work as a consultant, with only occasional trips for meetings. Part time, he also manages the Fellowship's finances and facilities. Their son, Evan, will soon turn 17, and is already looking at potential colleges. Their daughter, Beth, who recently turned 15 and acts like she's going on 24, runs the household, or thinks she does. Both kids have been active in the life of the Fellowship and have become very involved at Emmaus Community Church.

Soon, people even came from surrounding towns and other parts of the country to participate in classes and retreats. Even non-Christians would take time to walk the gardens and sense the Presence that made them feel safe. It wasn't too long before many of these visitors began to investigate further about what the Fellowship had to offer.

The Fellowship started a special training program, headed by Walter, intended to help people experience and cooperate with Jesus' Presence at their workplace. Even in Emmaus, work environments were supposed to be free from religious influence, especially any open discussion about church, and particularly about Jesus. Walter started the training program because, as he grew in his faith, he became increasingly frustrated with his own work environment. His entire company, and the whole business system for that matter, seemed to function as though God didn't even exist—much less live Present among His followers, desiring to guide them in the both technical and relational decisions of their profession. Walt had always known that, as a Christian, he should behave in a loving way toward others, and if asked, be prepared to share his faith. But he now realized that there needed to be more to living as a follower of Jesus in the workplace. It occurred to him that whatever product a business might be dealing with, Jesus ultimately originated it and knows how to make it work correctly. He also knows all a company's employees, customers, and competitors, and wants the best for all of them. What would it mean to follow Jesus as a businessperson, a professional, and an employee?

Walter discussed his concern with Lillian and they prayed that the Lord would reveal what he should do with this longing for himself and for others to experience Jesus' Presence at work. Eventually, Walter met other businessmen and women in Emmaus who had the same concern. Together they agreed to experiment with ways to take Jesus' Presence and Lordship seriously in their professional lives. Eventually, they developed what they called "The Business Day Rhythm."

The Rhythm contains a daily pattern which can be adapted to any work environment. The Business Day Rhythm recommends starting the day, whether at home, in the car, or at work, with prayers expressing one's utter dependence upon God. It invites us to recognize that the coming day will be influenced by forces and events impossible to predict; the implications of the day's actions and decisions will extend far beyond anyone's anticipation, affecting many people for good or evil.

The second phase of the Rhythm recommends a prayerful attentiveness to one's own thoughts and feelings and to those of others, recognizing that the Lord might be suggesting a certain question to consider or an action to be taken.

The Rhythm's third phase emphasizes the importance of doing one's very best, technically and relationally, believing that each person, whether recognizing it or not, represents Jesus in that place and has been called there to serve Him. Coworkers need to be affirmed and encouraged, and interpersonal conflict must be dealt with humbly and as soon as possible.

The Rhythm fourthly emphasizes an ongoing process of silent and non-verbal prayer throughout the day, continually asking for direction, confessing and releasing thoughts and actions that don't honor God, trusting the moment into His power and will. The Rhythm stands on the promise in Romans 8:28 that God will work everything for good for those who love Him and are called to serve Him, even in a secular business.

Walter and his team hold regular one-day seminars that include opportunities for people to discuss the situations they face in the marketplace, as well as to learn and adapt the Business Day Rhythm to their own context. The program encourages men and women to make covenant relationships with a few other Christians for encouragement and support.

While Lillian still provides some spiritual direction, she now functions more as the "mother" for the people who

221

volunteer at the Fellowship. She counsels the counselors, directs the directors, mentors the mentors, teaches the teachers and loves them all into a community that's learning to love and follow Jesus.

Spiritual community forms an important aspect of the Fellowship's training experience, enabling people to experience Jesus Present in a world that often functions with hostility toward Him. Lillian is often quoted, "We've learned that the Father adopts us into His family and Jesus makes Himself known to us; He guides us and empowers us in the context of that family. If you are to survive as a follower of Jesus, you must allow the Holy Spirit to guide you into relationship with a group of other followers where you can become attentive together to His Presence."

The Good Soil Farm

Barry, now grayer and frailer, says he has never felt more alive and productive. His farm reflects the same vibrancy. Where only grain fields once grew, now orchards, vineyards, and gardens flourish. The few cows and pigs he'd once housed in his barn have become herds of cattle, flocks of sheep, goats, and chickens, even a herd of horses and, of course, pigs. The barn has been expanded several times over. On the acreage near the house, several buildings with dormitories and meeting rooms have been constructed. The Good Soil Farm bustles six days a week with dozens of people.

Jesus had given Barry a particular burden for folks who felt like outsiders, who wouldn't have come to church to learn about Jesus Present. After Lillian and Jim helped him solidify his thoughts and dreams, Barry began to approach other farmers in the area, starting with his sons, Aaron and Ben. He poured out his concerns for those who would never even give church a try and who needed to experience the Presence of Jesus in practical ways in an open and accepting community, a place of beauty and living things. Barry told them that he'd thought about talking to the wardens of a men's prison and a women's prison not too far away about participating. He asked the boys to meet together with their wives and ask Jesus if He might be leading them to share this vision with him. It took some time and lots of discussions, but Aaron and Ben eventually sold their farms. They used the proceeds to buy into their dad's farm, to build new homes for themselves on the property, and to construct the first buildings to house people who would come to the Good Soil Farm.

Far before any plans were finalized or buildings built, Barry, Aaron, and Ben spent focused time in prayer, seeking specific instructions from Jesus. They wanted this farm to belong to the Lord, not in name only, but in the specifics of the way it was designed and run. They also knew that the vision represented far too great a challenge to accomplish on their own. If Good Soil Farm ever happened, miracle after miracle would be needed. Barry shared with his sons, and eventually with everyone in a leadership role at the Farm, what he had learned about waiting on the Lord, attending to His Presence, and following His leading faithfully. Of course the folks of OCP and the Fellowship prayed and listened with them. At first people expressed impatience to move forward, but they soon learned that Jesus proved in practice that He is Present and active as they followed Him one step at a time.

Meanwhile, Barry, with the support of Pastor Jim, talked to the Ministerial Association, the Elks Club, Kiwanis, and every group that would hear him out, asking for their participation and help. Before long, other nearby farmers agreed to do some of the work and supervise "workers in the field." They started with a few male convicts on Tuesdays and a few female convicts on Thursdays who, because of good behavior, were offered the opportunity to come and take on some aspect of the farm work. Each time they came, they were treated to a hot country dinner prepared by the local farmers. Before workers were invited to do any work, however, they attended classes on horticulture and farming with an emphasis on the wonder and grandeur of God's creation. No one told them they should believe in God; but the "workers in the field" soon discovered that this farm belonged to Jesus. Participants could pick which aspect of farm life they wanted to focus on, but they were expected to take a turn at everything.

Before a team started a task, the group leader always began by saying, "Let's ask the Boss what He'd like done today." The group would stand for a few minutes in silence and then the group leader would ask, "Get anything?" At first the inmates smirked and squirmed and no one "got anything." But within a few weeks, someone would pipe up with an idea about where to start or what felt most important. Soon, "asking the Boss" became not only a welcome custom, but often the beginning of a new adventure. When directions sometimes first appeared strange, they often became apparent later when the weather changed or a piece of machinery broke.

The use of teams formed an important part of the strategy at Good Soil Farm. Barry knew how isolated and lonely inmates could become. He'd seen the intimidating power structures among both guards and inmates at the prisons that cast shadows of fear and skepticism across their lives. Barry would watch the inmates at the farm and let the Lord show him which ones had potential to become leaders. He'd then invite them to become part of his own team and showed them how to "ask the Boss." He'd lead with compassion and model with his own hard work. When these men and women became ready, Barry would publicly acknowledge their achievements and assign them their own team. As a special sign of appreciation, every team member had the opportunity to take a portion of the produce back to the prison. That took some time consuming the "rule revisions" among the wardens. The fresh vegetables served as an advertisement for the Good Soil Farm and produced a waiting list for participation.

Of course, like Lillian, Barry faced many obstacles. He almost had to take the county to court to get them to reclassify his farm from agriculture to a nonprofit organization that would allow him not to pay taxes and to house workers on his property. The convicts themselves also proved to be a major challenge. Naturally even the best of them brought their wounds, relational disabilities, and work standards with them. Occasionally Barry would have to break up a fight or send someone back. To get people to work together, he even had to institute a competition between teams with awards for the most work done. After a few years the competition became unnecessary as the workers learned that hard work and helpful relationships actually felt rewarding and fun. Some of the local farmers expressed concern that Good Soil Farm might be a scam designed simply to make a big profit with cheap labor. Barry had to publish his books every year in the local newspaper and hire an independent accounting firm to satisfy them. There seemed to be no end to county, state, and federal regulations that addressed everything from bathrooms and kitchens to the size of signs. Finally the dorms were constructed to provide for people who traveled too far to commute and really participate. The housing produced no end of additional security problems and regulations.

In time, the prison system workers were joined by others needing that kind of community experience or who desired to help. College students, social work interns, inner-city homeless, and people doing community service mandated by the courts were eventually added to the residential and commuting community of Good Soil Farm. Eventually the volunteer and paid staff grew in numbers and competence so that Barry could spend most of his time encouraging and mentoring potential leaders the Lord pointed out to Him.

Many local families committed several hours a week or month to work and interact with the workers. In return they could take home a portion of the fruits, vegetables, and flowers. Alcoholics Anonymous and other recovery groups often "made a retreat" on the farm, volunteering help with the chores. Within a few years, the people of Emmaus began to "own" the work of the Good Soil Farm and felt a responsibility to take part, even if only to supportively mix with the folks who came there to work.

Good Soil Farm offered time for prayer and worship after lunch each day, although no one felt pressured to attend. However, people weren't on the Farm too long before they checked out the "meeting," and kept coming back. People, both workers and volunteers, soon gained a real sense that the "Boss" actively participated in the workings of the Farm and its family life. In the same way people in recovery programs discovered the reality of a "Higher Power," the Good Soil Farm workers and staff soon discovered that same Presence and many came to know Jesus personally.

Emmaus Community Church

It all started when Jim, Barry, and Lillian approached the Elder Board and shared how they'd been learning to experience Jesus' Presence, discovering how to actually follow Him instead of trying to figure out what to do themselves. Despite some skepticism among the Elders, Jim proposed that the Elder Board join them in a three-month experiment with Jesus. The three trusted that the experiment would demonstrate that Jesus would make His Presence known among them. Each Elder Board meeting would begin half an hour early in the church Sanctuary for prayer. They would check in about the things going on in their lives, and then spend ten minutes of silence, listening for what the Lord might have to say. Finally they would pray for one another as they felt the Lord's leading.

In the actual Board meeting, they agreed to spend another period of silence waiting for the Lord to speak to them about the topics they planned to discuss, before finalizing the agenda. The experiment specified that if, after three months, the rest of the Board didn't want to continue, Jim would agree to go back to the business model they had been using before. Jim even suggested that they bring in the rocking chair from his office, sharing that it had become a symbol that helped him remember that Jesus actually lives Present with them. Discussion ensued about good use of time, the fact that not all people are called as intercessors, and even that time for the new experiment couldn't eliminate the coffee and homemade cookies.

The Elder Board finally agreed. In much less than three months they discovered a new and vital dynamic in their Board meetings. Soon, no one questioned that Jesus made His Presence known in amazing ways. The rocking chair did provide a helpful symbol for the Elder Board. Sometimes they would discuss an issue, with all its pros and cons, readied for a vote, and someone would glance at the chair and remind the group that they'd not yet asked the Lord. Before long, the Board members experienced the meetings, once the pariah of their church life, as one of their most exciting and inspiring times.

The meetings' changes impacted the Board's life in a number of dimensions. First, Board members received ministry from the Lord and one another in the opening prayer time that set them free to fully participate in the meeting. Instead of entering the Board business with unresolved frustrations of the day, and the preference to be somewhere else, each person could briefly share their concerns and then receive the group's prayers for trust and release of their issues to the Lord. Then, in the meeting itself, the initial silent waiting time gave them opportunity to relinquish preconceived positions and biases on the topics of the meeting, freeing their minds and emotions for Jesus to truly lead the work they needed to do. Everyone felt surprised at the lightness they experienced in the meetings, even on difficult topics, and how quickly they were able to move through the agenda. During these weeks of experimentation, voting disappeared from the Board meetings. Everyone realized that the Lord wouldn't lead different people in different ways about the same matter. If they genuinely disagreed, it meant that they needed to seek the Lord more earnestly until all felt an affirmation for the direction they were to go. Even more importantly, they began to observe greater wisdom in their decisions, resulting in greater consensus and support in the congregation. Most of all, the Board members recognized that each meeting had been a participation in the Presence of God. They felt loved by God and were honored to serve Him in the life of the church.

Jim had not yet shared his visions for changes in the Sunday morning services. However, it didn't take long before several Elders began to question why Sunday mornings didn't exhibit the same vibrancy and sense of Presence that they experienced in the Board meetings. To Jim's surprise, no one blamed him; they all felt responsible that most of the congregation worshiped on Sunday as though Jesus weren't there. Jim shared some of his ideas about how to frame the different parts of the service in ways that would take Jesus' Presence more seriously. They agreed to "experiment" with worship, to see how the Lord might lead them. They would introduce changes slowly, preceded by an occasional "witness talk" from one of the Elder's experience of the Presence of Jesus, encouraging everyone to take Him seriously in that particular aspect of worship.

One of the Elders eventually suggested that the rocking chair might also be helpful on Sunday. They agreed to place it on the chancel for a few Sundays and one or two of them would explain how the Lord had used it to remind them of His Presence in their Board meetings. After its original introduction, the rocking chair became a permanent fixture. While no one treated it as holy or some sort of relic, neither were they surprised when someone placed a glass of water next to it, or even milk and cookies during the Christmas season.

Jim slowly introduced small changes in the church service which he had brainstormed with Barry and Lillian months earlier. He added a minute of silence at the beginning, with an invitation for the congregation to turn their attention to Jesus. Scripture readings were preceded with the acknowledgement that the Holy Spirit dictated the text with this gathering in mind, and that He would direct its truth to each person's unique situation. They followed the Scripture reading with a prayer of thanks and two minutes of silence to consider what the Lord might be saying to each one.

Jim's preaching usually focused on the Gospel lessons and people's actual experience of Jesus in the biblical story, as well as His promise to be with us always. Silence for personal reflection after the sermon became holy times of encounter and discovery. Jim often noticed people jotting notes toward the end of the time for prayer.

Hymns and choruses were chosen which expressed the truth of the text for the day. Often when the pronouns of the song were written in the third person, "He or Him," the congregation learned to spontaneously change them to "You." This simple change helped worshipers to personally interact with God and express the truths of the song for themselves. The congregation began to sing louder, with more passion, and tears of love or repentance often flowed.

Jim's method for sermon preparation also changed. For years previously, each sermon had been the pastor's personal and secret creation, only to be unveiled during the Sunday worship. Realizing how the Lord speaks more clearly, or at least people can often hear more clearly, in community, Jim began sharing his thoughts about the coming month's messages with the Elder Board. He invited their input, not so much about the content or style of the sermon, but the message focus related the needs within the congregation. Often the Elders confirmed the leading Jim had already felt from the Lord. Sometimes, however, Jim's question about the coming sermons would prompt discussion about the spiritual condition of the congregation or particular dynamics that the Lord might want to address. Jim ultimately remained free to construct his messages the way he thought best, but he often found that the wisdom that emerged proved to be a leading from the Lord. Not only did the sermons become better focused, but the Elders shared a responsibility to pray for both Jim's preparation and the congregation's receptivity. As the congregation gradually learned about these sermon dialogues in the Elder Board, people seemed to listen more carefully, not so much for a well-crafted exposition of the text, but for God's word to them personally.

Barry did get reelected to the Elder Board. In time, he suggested that they pray about adding a new ministry of prayers for healing after the service. Lillian had already begun to teach inner and physical healing at the Fellowship. She suggested ways they might train a prayer team to be available to anyone who wanted prayer. After some months of prayer and discussion, the Board agreed to proceed. No one would be pressured, but the ministry simply offered for those who were interested. To the Board's surprise a number of members jumped at the chance to be trained. The ministry started slowly, but before long many people regularly came for prayer. The healing of Jim and Kate's son, Brian, turned out to be the first major miracle they experienced, but not the last.

The "Jesus' Presence" movement wasn't restricted to Emmaus Community Church. From the very beginning Jim shared his hopes and dreams with the Ministerial Association and asked for their prayers and wisdom. The foundations for unity had been laid when he and Father Pat had first developed a relationship over golf. Other ministers in the community gradually joined. The monthly gathering cautiously started with only the study of a Scripture passage followed by a few surface prayers for the town and world. Over several months, as friendships were formed and strengthened, the group learned to trust one another and the safety of the group process. In time, some of these personal friendships spread into the pastors' congregations.

By the time Jim shared with the group of pastors his dream about people experiencing Jesus as really being Present, they were ready to listen with respect and interest. Not everyone found themselves on the same page by a long shot. Some expressed concern that Jim might be moving in the direction of Pentecostalism. The more liturgical church leaders feared he was suggesting a movement toward informal services that could get out of hand.

The Lord used Father Pat to bring the leaders together, however. He suggested that they ask the Lord what He wanted them to do; what part they should play in supporting Jim; and how Jesus might be directing their own churches? They all agreed to earnestly seek the Lord and to follow His leading as best they could understand it. The pastors began seeking God on these questions that very day as they stood in a circle, clasping hands. Each one thanked Jesus for His Presence, confessed their personal biases, asked Him for wisdom, and promised obedience with the help of the Holy Spirit. Years later the pastors often referred to that meeting as a turning point in their lives, their churches, and in the life of the whole town.

Jim's request for help prompted a significant shift in the ongoing ministerial meetings. From that time on, they gave time in each meeting for silence to become attentive to the Lord. Sometimes a question emerged from the discussion that they would take into prayer; other times, the group simply began with a time of listening and then shared what had come to mind. It didn't take long for everyone to realize that Jesus did in fact enter into the discussion with them, often giving one person a question or concern, another person a piece of the answer, and still another person a different piece. The spiritual leaders of Emmaus learned to experience Presence.

By the time that Lillian approached the Ministerial Association for their support for the Fellowship, they were ready. When Barry came a few months later, it turned out that the Lord had already spoken in a dream to one of the pastors about something very similar. In each case, they listened and promised to pray and then get back to them. The answer to both Lillian and Barry came as, "How can we help?"

Of course, the leaven sown in the ministerial group didn't stay there; it spread like a beautiful sunrise across the landscape of their congregations. A few of the congregations began to share seasonal services and eventually partnered in joint outreach ministries to the community and world. As various pastors experienced the personal Presence of Jesus in their times together and heard about Jim's experiments in his church, they slowly began to experiment within their own contexts. Simple adjustments, such as times of silence to listen and changing the pronoun from Him to You in a song or prayer, began to help people focus on the Lord and really expect Jesus to be involved in their worship experience. Of course, as soon as they began to look for Him, the Lord responded in all kinds of ways.

In some of the churches people felt skeptical about speaking of Jesus doing or saying this or that, fearful of subjectivism. But in time, and with the wise counsel of their pastors, people became more comfortable as they realized that seldom does one person hear from God perfectly and definitively. They discovered that we discern Him most clearly when we seek Him in twos and threes. Slowly but surely, most of the churches in Emmaus experienced a new vitality in worship, new power in prayer, and new compassion for those in need—Presence.

Emmaus

Adoption and transformation in the lives of so many of the people began to change the complexion of the town of Emmaus. Like most small towns, Emmaus always had its cliques and well-defined boundaries between the "in" people and the "out" people, the "haves" and the "have-nots." Even with several churches spotting the landscape, the unchurched population traditionally represented a majority. Although the environment was never openly hostile to faith, the religious jokes had prevailed as an important part of local humor. However, in the last ten years, things have begun to change.

For many, the traditional stereotypes about the religious and the irreligious have lost their black and white distinctions. Believers in Emmaus have come to understand that everyone travels on their own journey relative to God. Even though some seem to be stuck or moving in the wrong direction, followers of Jesus learned to trust the Holy Spirit's work and watched for how they might cooperate. They knew through experience that God loves each person and works to bring them into His Kingdom. As Christians stopped judging non-Christians, the non-Christians seemed to respond in kind. The less "outsiders" felt pressure to become "insiders," the more comfortable they became participating in functions at the Farm or even the Fellowship. Jesus became real to many long before they ever attended church.

Denominational barriers began to break down, as well. While some church groups once felt that they represented the only true and faithful version of Christianity, the ongoing cooperation and interaction between churches brought about more understanding and less judgment. People began to realize that, although the forms might vary and theological and doctrinal differences might still be very real, most Christians really do believe in Jesus and want to love and serve Him. Jesus' Lordship and Presence became the cornerstone for how people understood Christianity rather than the distinctions between church practices or doctrines. As these followers of Jesus gained more compassion and respect for one another, a new climate of love and acceptance emerged in the town of Emmaus, as a whole. People felt free to hold their differences in personal theology, values, and church preference without judgment or condemnation. Judgment and condemnation were left to God.

When people visited the Fellowship, the Farm, one of the community projects, or even one of the churches in town, seldom were they asked whether or not they were believers. Christians recognized that visitors wouldn't be there unless

Jesus drew them, so they just trusted Jesus to bring them along in His own way. Believers also became more apt to frequent a pub for dinner in addition to the nonalcoholic cafes. They made friends and demonstrated the Presence of Jesus in loving ways. "Pre-believers" felt respected for who they were and where they were in process.

Christians weren't shy about their faith, however. Even in the pub they weren't hesitant to pray before meals or talk about their life with Jesus and the projects He'd started in Emmaus. It became common to ask pre-believers to join in and help, recognizing that most people need to experience the truth before they can believe it.

The way this small town focused on the poor also changed. In fact, you might say one can't really find "poor" in Emmaus, in the extreme sense, at least. No one sleeps on the streets or under bridges or begs on the corner. Rooms at the Rescue Mission or the Farm provide welcome shelter when someone finds themselves destitute. Interestingly, people who are gripped by crisis or who come to town with nothing seldom stay that way. The Chamber of Commerce, in collaboration with the Ministerial Association, endeavors to find work of some kind for anyone who needs it. The Chamber collaborates with the local high school to provide evening classes designed to help people gain skills that will make them more employable. They set up a city fund to help employers hire under-skilled workers until they can be trained. Both the Farm and the Fellowship oversee a number of recovery and treatment programs to help those with addictions and mental illnesses. Of course there are always those that don't want or won't accept the help, but often loving persistence from the community helps them gain new hope which encourages them to try.

The divorce rate and unwed pregnancy rate in Emmaus have dropped dramatically. The Fellowship partners with the schools to offer courses and support groups related to parenting and personal development. The community mindset has changed from criticizing failure to offering help and preventing desperate situations when possible. The Fellowship's mentor training has proved especially helpful in this area. Mentors, trained in listening and support skills, make themselves available to anyone who has a need. The town looks primarily to the churches to provide these mentors and to make referrals. Non-faith-based groups also feel comfortable referring people for mentoring, knowing that the mentees will not be browbeaten with guilt or pressured to join a church. Seldom, however, has anyone emerged from a mentoring relationship without firsthand experience of Jesus' Presence.

Emmaus' population has also become more vibrant and youthful. When Jesus first appeared to Jim, Lillian, and Barry, high school graduates "got out of town" just as soon as they could. Without a college or good jobs for young people, why should they stay? But today, the Fellowship, the Farm, and the churches attract a flood of young interns and volunteers desiring to explore the innovations emerging in Emmaus. The Fellowship alone supervises half a dozen social work and seminary interns. The state university provides students and professors to help the Farm operate with the latest technology and agriculture expertise. Seminaries send their brightest students to experience the "experimental" forms of church they find in Emmaus. With the influx of young adults, youth ministry flourishes. In a cooperative effort, local churches, and businesses have begun to cater to the younger crowd. There's even talk about establishing a Community College branch in Emmaus. Today, a young person might just tell you that Emmaus is a fun place to live! The reality of adoption and transformation, although not part of the usual vocabulary of its citizens, is powerfully felt. Jesus called it the Kingdom of God.

ఐఐ ఇఇ

Well, back to the celebration at the Good Soil Farm on the tenth anniversary of Jesus' appearance. Barry, Lillian, and Jim stood together in a circle made up of the rest of the Order.

Around them stood other leaders of the various ministries of the community and around them stood hundreds of those who have participated in some way. No one but the three knew why this date had been picked specifically, but it had been declared a day of celebration for all that God had done among them, and everyone turned out who could come. A local music group led worship; two people read appropriate portions of Scripture over a portable PA system, and Barry recounted the history of Good Soil Farm for the crowd and on-looking cameras. Barry shared about the ways that his own life had been changed by Jesus, about the Lord's desire to demonstrate His Presence and love to people in practical ways, and thanked the community of Emmaus for their support in making that possible at the Farm. After his short but moving talk, Barry invited the whole assembly into a time of silent adoration and praise, reflecting on their own journey with Jesus—Present. The sun shone brightly with just the right spring warmth, and the breeze in the newly leafed trees rustled and whispered, as everyone joined hands and stood in silence, letting their hearts do the praying.

As Jim, Barry, and Lillian clasped their hands, they felt a growing warmth, as if another Source of heat radiated between their touch. As the heat radiated up their arms and into their chests, they felt as though their hearts enlarged with a buoyancy that might lift them off the ground. Finally, Barry shouted out with his booming voice, "Jesus stands here with us and He's delighted! You have all given Him great joy!" The crowd responded with applause and cheers that rang with depth and breadth and beauty that extended into regions far beyond the town of Emmaus – into Heaven itself!

Following the kind of grand banquet that only a potluck can provide, Jim, Lillian, and Barry strolled together down the dirt road that wandered toward town. They walked silently for almost a mile, reflecting on the amazing events that had occurred over the last ten years and wondering what the Lord might do next. They shared many stories of struggle and despair followed by the Lord's victory, often experienced in unexpected ways. In retrospect they saw that God had a plan all along but had only given them glimpses about the next step. Just as He had done in their face-to-face meetings, Jesus always led one step ahead of them, inviting them to trust Him and venture forward in faith.

Lillian changed the subject from the past to the future. "You know, as much as I love being part of what Jesus is doing now, I find myself longing to be with Him in heaven. I'd love to see His ruddy complexion and those amazing eyes again."

Jim broke in, "And feel His hug."

Barry continued, "How I look forward to walking with Him through the fields and forests of heaven. I've imagined that I could communicate with the plants and animals in mutual admiration and love."

Jim whispered, "Can you imagine standing with Jesus and being introduced to the Father, and realizing that we've known Him all along? What will it be like to see the Holy Spirit and feel the winds of His life flowing through us?"

Lillian concluded, "I see us standing with the Trinity, looking over our lives and all that has taken place, celebrating the amazing love and wisdom of God. We'll see the mysteries of what He's done—His Presence. Looking at everything that seemed so confusing and even contradictory, I think I'll simply respond, 'Of course!'"

The three continued their walk, turning to take a shortcut back to the Farm. On their right they saw an abandoned farmhouse that had been empty for decades. As they approached, they saw on its porch a small table draped with a bright yellow tablecloth and set with a vase of flowers and what looked like makings for a tea party. Curiosity got the best of them, so they turned aside and walked to the porch. Here, in fact, stood the table, four chairs, and the tea setting. A plate of freshly baked scones adorned a center platter next to a piping hot pot of tea.

Barry exclaimed, "What a wonderful surprise! I'll bet one of my daughters-in-law set this out to surprise us!"

Lillian motioned to the table, "Well, let's not disappoint them. Let's sit down."

Barry, Lillian and Jim each took a chair at the beautifully set table. Lillian poured the tea and passed the cream and sugar. Barry helped himself to a scone, lathered it with butter, took a big bite and almost shouted, "It's orange; I knew my girls had a hand in this!"

Jim tasted his scone and turned to Barry. "They're cherry, not orange."

Lillian stared and then tasted her scone. Barry and Jim said in unison, "Coriander?"

Tears of joy ran down their cheeks, as they silently sipped the tea and nibbled the scones. They all now knew Who had prepared the table, prepared the tea, and baked the scones.

Suddenly, Lillian whispered, "Look," pointing to the fourth chair as it rocked back and forth. They hadn't noticed until now that the fourth chair was a rocking chair. They wondered if Jesus would appear sitting in the rocking chair and join them in tea and scones. They desperately hoped He would.

Barry broke the silence when he pointed to the road and gasped, "There!"

Before them, a short distance down the road, stood Jesus dressed in the same white robe and golden crown that He'd worn in their last visit. He was surrounded in and emanated the same bright light that accompanied His disappearance ten years ago. Jesus waived and beamed with the same broad smile they'd grown to adore. "Follow Me!" He shouted, "It's only just begun!"

They rose from their seats, walked to the road, and watched as Jesus became enveloped in the most glorious light that surrounded them in every direction. In what appeared like clouds of radiant color, they could almost make out what might be angel choirs, millions of people, and a large throne dazzling in light. Jesus waved, smiled again, and disappeared slowly into that light and beauty. Soon, the whole vision began to dissipate like a light snowfall of sparkling particles making everything around them glisten with life. The three stood and stared. Finally, Jim choked through tears and the lump in his throat, "You see, Heaven too, is Present."

For this reason I bow my knees before the Father,

from whom every family in heaven and on earth derives its name,

that He would grant you, according to the riches of His glory,

to be strengthened with power through His Spirit in the inner man,

so that Christ may dwell in your hearts through faith;

and that you, being rooted and grounded in love,

may be able to comprehend with all the saints

what is the breadth and length and height and depth,

and to know the love of Christ which surpasses knowledge,

that you may be filled up to all the fullness of God.

Now to Him who is able to do far more abundantly beyond all that we ask or think,

according to the power that works within us,

to Him be the glory in the church and in Christ Jesus to all generations forever and ever.

Amen.

Ephesians 3:14-21

Epilogue:

In writing the preceding pages, I found myself in tears many times as my heart longed to experience God in a tangible way that a physical encounter would provide. It seems to me that our Maker planted that same longing deep within our souls, and therefore any "distant" relationship with God results in a kind of spiritual pain. This painful desire for more of God can either drive us away from God in an attempt to avoid it, or the pain can move us toward Him in the hope that the Ephesians prayer above speaks more than a wishful invitation, but a dynamic promise of fulfillment. Assuming that you've made it through *Presence* and not just jumped to the end, I'll guess that you're up for the journey forward with Jesus; you're willing to risk that God's invitation leads to a wonderful fulfillment. Fantastic!

However, the journey to a deep and intimate experience of the love of God in His Presence can be an elusive one to many. Just trying harder at the things that have left Jesus "up there," and us "down here," will only produce the same separated results. Just as Lillian, Barry, and Jim had to learn to experience Jesus as Present, we also need to become students of the Holy Spirit and let Him guide us into a new intimacy with the Trinity. Fortunately we're not alone in our quest; Jesus followers have been learning how to follow the Holy Spirit on this journey since the very beginning. Not only does Scripture point the way to this dynamic and personal relationship, but men and women over the centuries have recorded what they've learned about adoption and transformation. The writings of the Desert Fathers and Mothers in the early centuries and later Church Fathers and Mothers can be used by the Holy Spirit to guide us forward to discern the miracle of Jesus with us— Present.

Today a major movement in Christian history called "spiritual formation" is sweeping the Church. God is calling believers to discover Him beyond religious practices into a deep level of relationship that will equip us to stand with Him in the face of the whirlwind of the Kingdom's coming. We're learning "spiritual disciplines" that help us to become more attentive to His Presence and available to His transformational work in our hearts. Followers of Jesus are learning how to listen more in prayer rather than just telling God how to run the universe. We're discovering that "waiting on the Lord" speaks more about a focus of the heart than it does about mere patience. Christians are finding that "community" can transcend "food and fellowship" into a life-changing experience of Jesus together—Present. To experience what we long for in our relationship with God, we all need to become life-long learners—of our Lord Jesus, fulfilling His prayer that we might all become one with Him, with the Father, and with one another.

This journey of discovery and transformation takes time. My own Christian walk started at age 22 while a student at Arizona State University. Eventually my professional career as an aerospace engineer gave way to years in the pastorate. But only after a decade serving churches was I exposed to life-long discipleship or what we now call spiritual formation. Through a friendship with a Trappist monk, Brother Boniface, I became immersed in the writings I mentioned above. God showed me the painful longing within me and I began to intentionally spend time in prayer learning to become attentive to Jesus' Presence rather than just trying to get something out of Him for my life or ministry. While I am still just a beginner, I can now write about what it would be like to experience Jesus' Presence because I have experienced it. While I have never seen Him physically or heard His audible voice, I am learning to discern Him abiding with me—right with me. So can you.

If *Presence* has stirred your heart, hold on to His subtle whispers of invitation with all your strength. Don't let yourself forget what your heart longs for. Don't get so busied with the next task or book that you return to a life that may well end up in heaven but which bores you to tears in the meantime. Stand intentionally with the apostle Paul who said,

> I press on so that I may lay hold of that for which also I was laid hold of by Christ Jesus. Brethren, I do not regard myself as having laid hold of it yet; but one thing I do: ...forgetting what lies behind and reaching forward to what lies ahead, I press on toward the goal for the prize of the upward call of God in Christ Jesus (Phil 3:12-14).

Where might you start? Consider using *Discovering Christ's Presence: A Study Guide for Presence,* published as a companion to this book. Whether you use it alone or in a group, the reflection questions and spiritual exercises can become rich opportunities for the Holy Spirit to "teach you all that Jesus has said."

I would also suggest that you read my book, *Mansions of the Heart: The Seven Stages of Spiritual Growth*, which describes the journey of spiritual growth that the Holy Spirit uses to lead us more and more deeply into the heart of God's love. You'll also find the *Mansions Study Guide* a great tool to discover your own place in the journey and the experience of His Presence.

Spiritual formation communities and ministries are being formed by God around the world to provide personal help and resources for individuals and churches who long to know and experience Jesus more personally. For example, I live as part of a covenant community called The Order of *Imago Christi*. We provide coaching and resources for Christian leaders and churches. One resource, a three day retreat experience called "Spiritual Formation Discovery for Leaders," provides an opportunity for participants to gain insight into their longing for God in the context of their own life history and learn how to cooperate with Him in their own spiritual growth. *Imago Christi* also develops resources to help you along the way and provides an extensive bibliography formatted for your particular place in the journey. On the *Imago Christi* website, you will also find links to a number of other spiritual formation ministries around the world.

Thank you for sharing this journey of discovery with me, through reading *Presence*, and through loving our Lord. I pray that your ongoing experience of Jesus may be as real and tangible as those described in this novel and that you may come to know personally the adoption and transformation that launches you into the fullness of abundant life. It's what God wants for you. Jesus lives here with you—Present—to make it possible.

Your brother in His Presence,

Tom Ashbrook.

COMPANION STUDY GUIDE

Presence has been designed for an individual reader or,

using the Study Guide, for group reading and discussion. The extensive use of Scripture makes the set a perfect tool for Bible study groups, using the story line to draw the participants into the truths of God's word and their application to their lives. This resource will be tremendously useful for church and ministry leaders who want to invite members into a deeper relationship with the Lord, members who may not yet realize that greater intimacy with the Lord is what their hearts long for.

See www.TomAshbrook.com for developing resources and dialogue with others using *Presence* and the *Presence Study Guide*.

New Spiritual Formation Resource for Spiritual Directors and Congregations

By R. Thomas Ashbrook

Mansions of the Heart: Exploring the Seven Stages of Spiritual Growth uses Teresa of Avila's seven mansions to explore the life-long journey of spiritual growth. While *Mansions* has been used with great success by seminaries, spiritual formation programs, and Christian leaders, the *Mansions Study Guide,* by Tom Ashbrook and Ted Wueste now makes *Mansions* accessible to small groups and spiritual direction relationships. This interactive study for personal reflection and group discussion enables Jesus followers to discover where they are in their journey of spiritual growth and learn how to cooperate with the Holy Spirit's transformation work.

See www.mansionsoftheheart.com for ordering information and discounts.

CRM EMPOWERING LEADERS

CRM (Church Resource Ministries: www.crmleaders.org) is a movement committed to developing leaders to strengthen and multiply the Church worldwide.

More than three hundred and fifty CRM missionaries live and minister in nations on every continent, coaching, mentoring, and apprenticing those called to lead the Christian movement in their settings. This results in the multiplication of godly leaders who have a passion for their work and who are empowered to multiply their lives and ministry. Through them, CRM stimulates movements of fresh, authentic churches, holistic in nature, so that the name of God is renowned among the nations. See www.crmleaders.org. Tom Ashbrook serves with CRM as the leader of the Order of *Imago Christi*. See www.crmleaders.org.

The Order of *Imago Christi* forms CRM's spiritual formation ministry to Christian leaders around the world. At *Imago Christi's* core lies a covenant community that develops spiritual formation resources and coaches leaders and churches to be able to live and lead with a spiritual authority grounded in loving intimacy with Jesus. Tom Ashbrook founded Imago Christi and plays an integral part in leading this community. See www.ImagoChristi.org.

Made in the USA
San Bernardino, CA
14 August 2020